Jay Leno, on Electric Vehicles:

"If you're in a quiet, electric vehicle, you're not polluting and you're saving," said Leno. "When I want to have fun, I'll take out my 1960 Triumph TR3 and bomb around, but in terms of everyday vehicles, you can't beat [the Tesla]."
— Jay Leno, on CNBC's The News with Shepard Smith, Dec 18 2020
https://www.cnbc.com/2020/12/18/jay-leno-reveals-what-he-thinks-is-the-genius-behind-elon-musk-tesla.html

Jay Leno, on Electric Vehicle Conversions:

"I look at it this way: If it makes the car better, safer, more reliable and faster—and you can change it back to stock whenever you want—why not do it?"
— Jay Leno, on restomods, Popular Mechanics

James May, on Modernizing Classic Cars:

"The thing that most people like about classic cars is they way the look. [...] They're part of the history of art and design, and people want to celebrate that. So why not electrify them to make them more usable? A lot of people think they want a Ferrari Daytona, but that's because they haven't driven one. They don't realize that it's a complete tractor. Most people want to drive around looking cool, so why not?"
— James May, on Drivetribe, YouTube
https://www.youtube.com/watch?v=O9yCOCufjDA

Overheard at an Environmentalists Convention:

"If we're going to be serious about climate change and saving energy, we should stop melting down old cars to make new ones and just recycle them as they are. What's the point of melting down a perfectly good car just because the engine is lousy? Clean it up, slap an electric motor in it and be on your way in style."
— Eleanor Roosevelt, in conversation with Nicola Tesla, (probably)

Convert It!

A Simple Step-By-Step Guide
For Converting any Classic Car
Into an Electric Vehicle

(For fun or profit!)

By Ron L. Toms

All information in this book was researched and presented here to the best of my
knowledge and ability. No guarantees or warranties are made regarding the
accuracy or suitability of the information in this book for any purpose.
It is likely that there will be errors and mistakes contained herein.
Please do your own research and proceed at your own risk.
The author is not a licensed professional engineer.
The author is not a professional mechanic.
The author is not a certified electrician.
For entertainment purposes only.
Your mileage may vary.
Please be careful.
Have fun!
<==>
*

Published by Ronald L. Toms
Visit www.RLT.com for more information

ISBN: 978-1-946767-03-5

Contents:

Section One:

The Wordy Parts

(To read, or not to read, that is your discretion.)

Introduction

You could go out and buy a brand-new electric car. You'll spend somewhere between $30,000 and $200,000 and have a car that's pretty much just like all the others on the road. But what if you could get all the benefits of classic car styling **and** the benefits of an electric car for under $30,000? Maybe even half that much.

You can. The only catch is that you have to do the work yourself. That's what I did.

At first the project was daunting, almost paralyzing. But a few months of research followed by rolling up my sleeves and diving in head first changed the project from teetering on incomprehensible, to not-so-hard, then easy, and finally to "Ok, now I'm ready for another one!"

I didn't hesitate. I bought my second project car before the first one was even finished.

My project took seven months, working one day a week. If I'd had this book before I started I could have done it in a fraction of that time. You'll get the benefit of all my research and experience.

Rather than try to review all the products and options in the world — something that can easily be found with a simple Internet search — I decided it would me more helpful to walk you through the decisions process and expose the pitfalls and other things you may not have considered in a project like this.

Converting a car from gas to electric is a pretty big project, but if you have a good set of tools and good mechanical skills, you can do it. Along the way you'll need to fabricate some important pieces, like new motor mounts and battery boxes, among other things. If you're comfortable with steel work this won't be much of a challenge, and if you're not, aluminum is soft enough to be machined with woodworking tools. It is lightweight, which has advantages, and it won't rust. These are a few reasons why Aluminum is more commonly used in these projects than steel, but either one is acceptable.

The downsides to aluminum are that's it's more expensive than steel, and because it's softer than steel you'll have to use thicker pieces — which amplifies the extra cost a bit. As with everything, there are trade-offs. Only you can decide which is right for your situation.

My 14 year old son and I did our conversion in a tight one-car garage using only a complete socket and wrench set, screwdrivers, some hand-held power tools and a small drill press. We used a hand-held jigsaw to cut aluminum panels for our battery boxes. The one and only special purpose tool we bought was a hoist to remove the old engine, but there are a lot of ways to do this, and some cars (such as the classic VW Beetle with the rear engine) a standard floor-jack works great for engine removal.

Of course, there will be a lot of wiring to do too. You'll need wire strippers, connectors, probably crimpers too (depending on what kind of connectors you use), and a multi-function voltmeter is essential for checking your circuits. Remember, some will be 12-volt, some will be higher. Mine is 144 volts, but yours may be different.

You'll need to know your way around a car — where the fuse box is, how relays work and why you need them, how to get behind the dashboard, remove an engine and transmission, and a few other things.

Does it sound intimidating yet? If not, congratulations! This should be an easy project for you. If all that sounds daunting, don't worry. If you have moderate mechanical aptitude and take your time, you can do it. This book will give you step-by-step instructions wherever possible.

Of course, some things will be depend on what specific kind of car you're converting and how you want it to perform. I can't cover every detail or this book would be an encyclopedia of every type of car ever made. You'll have to figure some things out for yourself.

Like most things that are worthwhile, converting an old, classic car to electric can be a difficult and often tedious process. You will make mistakes. There will be times you'll wish you'd never started, but at the end, the smile on your face and the pride in your heart will erase all those doubts. Then, like me, you'll be looking at old cars a little differently from then on.

The Big Disclaimer

1. This book wasn't written for your exact situation. I guarantee there will be things here that you think are so obvious it's almost insulting. There will also be things you'll wish had been explained in greater detail. And those two things will be completely different, even reversed, for a lot of other people. I've tried to be as general and as complete as possible within the limits of my humble, human capabilities. My apologies if I've failed in that task.

2. The technology for motors, batteries and the other components for Electric Vehicles is a rapidly changing field. Everything in this book is as accurate as I can make it at the time of this writing (April, 2021), but I make no guarantees about the future other than this one — things are guaranteed to change.

New developments in battery technology are the most exciting, but it doesn't look like anything significant will hit the market until at least 2025 or 2030 or later. I would love to be wrong about that. Batteries are the biggest obstacle to electric cars. They contribute the greatest weight, the greatest cost, and take up the most space. We're just one new breakthrough away from solving all those problems.

Motor technology is more mature and less likely to change much. The big problem here is simple physics. To get a more powerful motor requires more voltage. High voltage can be extremely dangerous and should be left to professionals with the proper safety equipment, tools, and most importantly, training. This begs the question; "What do we mean by 'high' voltage. How much is too much?"

Household voltage in the USA is 120 volts. This doesn't seem to cause much trouble. In Europe and most of the rest of the world household voltage is 200 or higher. Again, without much trouble. High performance car companies like Tesla, VW, GM and others use much higher voltages, up to 700 volts and more. For the DIY EV builder, 144 volts seems to be the optimal answer. Higher voltage used equipment is available from salvaged Tesla, Chevy, Nissan and other EVs, but I'd recommend extreme caution or the help of a professional if you choose these options.

3. For now, EV conversion is very much a tinkerers world. This book cannot cover every situation or condition you will encounter. There is a lot of fabrication involved, conduits to run, wiring diagrams to decipher, measuring, planning, designing, re-designing and like every engineering project, numbers to crunch. You're going to have to figure a lot of things out on your own. And you will make mistakes. Some of them will cost more money than you thought it should.

If you're not comfortable with that, there are a number of professional shops who specialize in these conversions. If you have the cash, are short of free time and have a low threshold for frustration, taking your car to a specialty shop is probably worth it.

4. This project will take longer than you think. How long with it take? That depends on you. I studied mechanical engineering in college. I know enough about electricity to wire an entire house and install any size of solar power system, both grid connected and off-grid. I have rebuilt car engines, restored old cars and designed massive catapults, trebuchets and other mechanical devices for TV shows and commercials.

I expected my first EV car conversion to take a few weeks. It ended up taking seven months.

To be fair, most of that time was spent waiting for parts to arrive during the Covid-19 pandemic. I also didn't do much work during the summer. No one wants to die in an un-air-conditioned garage during a heat wave. And I had a lot of questions and few answers. Waiting for return phone calls from vendors, emails that never came, missing computer files, bad web links, etc. (this was still very much a hobbyist endeavor at the time) and home-schooling my kids during the pandemic all greatly extended the time it should have taken.

I also spent a LOT of time watching countless Youtube videos, searching for specific pieces of information I needed and couldn't find amid all the irrelevant information in them. I've eliminated all the noise from those videos and distilled the useful information into this book. I sincerely hope it helps!

Maybe you'll do better than I did. Maybe you won't. In either case, having this book as a reference should help. And once completed, your efforts will be rewarded and you'll be glad you did it. It is a good project and definitely worth doing. At least, that was my experience. As always, your mileage may vary. (As well as your levels of frustration, anxiety, thrill, pride and enthusiasm, among others.)

About the car used in this book

My first conversion project was a 1960 Triumph TR3.

I didn't originally intend to convert the car. I drove one of these in college and absolutely loved it. As an adult, I found one in good condition at a reasonable price, so I bought it to drive and relive the glory days of my youth.

The car broke down almost immediately.

It was constantly overheating. New parts were ordered and I spent a few weeks upgrading the cooling system. It only lasted ten days before breaking down again. This time it was more serious. The carbs were getting gas, and the spark was working. I asked a mechanic to look at it. As soon as he learned the age of the car he backed out. I took it to someone else. Same story. I tracked down someone from the local Triumph club, but the advice he gave seemed more designed to show off his own knowledge than to be genuinely helpful.

I kept tinkering. And tinkering. But I could not get that engine to start.

I also have a small woodworking shop. One day I realized I hadn't used my radial arm saw in more than a decade. Honestly, I don't know why those things exist. It scared the crap out of me to use it—which is why I never did. It always felt like I was one false move from cutting my hand off.

I decided to sell the saw, but I didn't know if it still worked after all those years sitting idle in a barn. I plugged-in the motor and switched it on. It came to life just like it was brand new. Try letting a gas engine sit in a barn for ten years and see how easy it is to start. That's also the annual problem I have with my lawn mower. It's always a chore to get it to start that first time after winter storage.

After the lesson from my radial arm saw I decided to get an electric lawn mower and see if I liked it. Long story short — It was a beautiful experience. Quiet, clean, easy, reliable. That's what convinced me to convert the TR3 to an Electric Vehicle. What's the use of having such a beautiful car just to take-up space in your garage? I bought it to drive, not to be garage candy.

But it meant my classic car wouldn't be pure anymore. It felt sacrilegious. When I drove one in college, it was sporty and fast. Would an electric motor give me that same experience? Looking up the specs in the owner's manual surprised me. Right out of the factory a TR3 had a zero-to-sixty MPH time of twelve seconds, and a top speed of one hundred miles per hour.

My Toyota 4Runner does better than that.

It was time to do some side-by-side comparison. I picked a popular electric motor and created a table.

	Triumph motor	Netgain Hyper-9 HV
Torque:	1400 in-lbs (117 ft.-lbs.)	220 Nm (162 ft.-lbs.)
Max Power:	77 HP	90 kW (120 HP)
Max RPMs:	5000	8000
Weight:	320 lbs.	130 lbs.
Size:	27" x 17" x 28"	9" x 9" x 14"
Moving Parts:	Over a thousand.	One (the rotor).
Maintenance:	Oil, Water, Antifreeze, Filters, Tune-ups…	None.
Breakdowns:	Frequent and unexpected.	None anticipated.

It seemed like a no-brainer. Then I remembered, motors don't run without fuel.

Fuel:	Gasoline	Electrons
Volume:	15 gallons (2.2 cubic ft.)	20 kWh (7.5 cu. ft.)
Weight:	105 lbs.	330 lbs.
Range: (approx.)	270 - 300 miles	80 - 100 miles

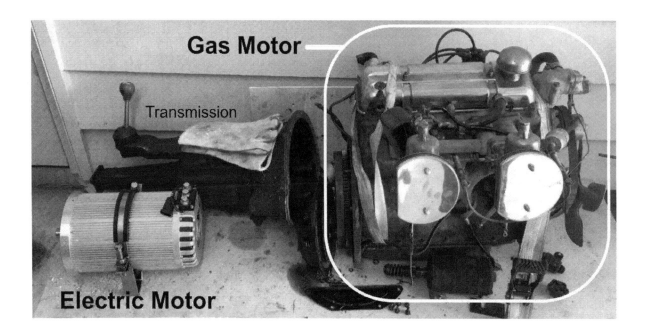

Gas Motor

Transmission

Electric Motor

The electric motor is *MUCH* smaller. As you can see, it's even smaller than the transmission. If we replaced the transmission with the electric motor we'd have the whole engine compartment for batteries. This may not be a good idea (we'll explain why later), but we'll still have plenty of open space under the hood for batteries, and the rest can go where the gas tank used to be. So the volume didn't make any difference.

And the weight difference is a wash. Engine plus fuel for both is within 3.5%. All the removed gas components came to 425 lbs. Electric components added came to 440 lbs. The difference is about the weight of a small, packed suitcase.

That leaves the real trade-off: Reduced range in exchange for better performance and rock-steady reliability. Plus the benefit of no noise, no exhaust odors or oil drips, no going to the gas station, and in all honesty, driving one of these more than fifty miles is something I very rarely did.

We're back to no-brainer territory.

I placed an order for the motor.

That's when the reality of the other downside hit. Converting to EV can be expensive. Ignoring the value of my labor, I spent a total of $18,000 on parts and equipment to upgrade a car that had a street value of $17,000 before the conversion. But, keep in mind I chose top-of-the-line everything for this project. Cost was no object. I wanted a car I could keep and rely on forever. You can do it cheaper.

I justified the cost by blaming on my son. He's fourteen years old and wants to be a robotics engineer. This will be his introduction to power systems and mechanical engineering. The cost of the project will come out of his college fund.

He can thank me later.

How much will this project actually cost you?

You should understand this is a rapidly changing market and anything I say will almost certainly be outdated as soon as this book is published. So, with the caveat that your mileage may vary, here are some basics of cost.

The Donor Car— You're on your own here. Some folks have started with a junked MGB they acquired off craigslist for as little as $500. Others have started with a fully-featured brand-new kit car that cost as much as a new car right from the showroom floor. For your first project, keep it as simple as possible, but make it a car you actually *want* to drive. You're going to put a lot of time into the project. Make it an investment. But don't worry too much about finding the perfect car. The beauty of an electrical drive system is that all the expensive components can be easily transplanted into another project later if you want. The only thing you lose is the time you've invested.

My first project started with a $17,000 TR3. My second one was a 1959 VW Bug in great condition I picked up for $7000. My third will be either a 2005 Mustang or a 1940's era pick-up truck. Maybe both?

The Batteries— With the possible exclusion of the donor car, (and excluding any technological disruption in the market), the batteries will be your single largest expense. The only real trade-off is range, but maximum acceleration can be affected as well. This will be limited by the discharge amps your battery can dump—called the C-rate. We'll discuss this in the chapter on batteries. In general, more than half the cost of your upgrade will be for the batteries. At the time of this writing (and making some extremely general assumptions about your car and your driving habits), batteries will cost between $80 to $120 per mile of range. But that will eventually change. Batteries are getting better and prices are dropping every year.

The Motor— Don't skimp here. Sure, you can save a little money with a lesser motor, but you're going to put a lot of work into this project and you'll want the result to be worthwhile. The motor is not your biggest expense, but it is the heart and soul of the performance you'll get. The top-of-the-line motors for most DIY projects are currently the Netgain Hyper-9 HV motor or the HPEVS 50/51 models. Budget around $4500 for either one. There are cheaper options: used motors out of forklifts, or an older Nissan Leaf or Tesla motor for example. Used motors are a rapidly moving target, and books like this are notoriously static. They can be a LOT cheaper, but you'll have to do your own homework if you choose a used motor.

Other Things— You'll need a state-of-charge display (this is like the gas gauge for your batteries). Also a charger, a charge controller, a battery management system, a DC-to-DC converter for bridging your high voltage and 12v systems, and if you plan on driving your car fast and hard all the time, you'll need a cooling system for the controller and batteries too, but this is optional. Mine are all air-cooled and it works fine.

Remember, your batteries are your biggest investment and also the easiest to abuse. Treat them well, buy them the right support equipment and it will be worth it. Budget another $1500 to $2,500 (or so) for these items.

Bottom Line— During the Covid months of 2020, my total cost for a classic convertible EV sports car was $35,000 (rounded).

Here's the breakdown:

$17,000 for the car. This included a fully functional, working gas engine when bought. If you want to do it cheaper, look for a "roller project" (A rolling project is a car with a non-functional engine or missing engine. Just make sure the suspension, steering and brakes are in good working order, and rust is minimal — especially on the underside of the car.)

$7000 for battery

$4500 for motor and controller

$3500 for battery management system, in-dash display, charge controller, charger, J1772 portable charging station, DC-to-DC converter (144 volts to 12 volts for normal car stuff like lights, radio, etc.), miscellaneous wire, relays, switches, dashboard indicator lights, etc.

$3000 for custom fabricated motor mounts, transmission coupler and adapter plate, custom battery boxes, conduits, replaced all lights with LEDs, added a new rack and pinion steering system (personal choice, not really needed), custom wood-grain dashboard, new mirrors, and a fancy shift knob. But I crafted a lot of the custom parts myself and I didn't account for the value of my time.

Worth it? Barring any unfortunate accidents, this car will last forever and will never go out of style. It will only go up in value over the years. I have zero regrets, and I absolutely love all the attention I get. My kid learned enough to teach his scoutmaster a few things when he got his automotive merit badge, and he's well on his way to becoming a robotics engineer.

Would I do it again? Already started on the '59 VW Bug. Now that I know what I'm doing, I can probably bring this one in around $22,000 total cost, including the original car.

Pros and cons of converting
a classic car to electric

Some of the reasons you SHOULD convert:

1. Reliability. Old classic cars break down constantly. They'd be a lot more fun if they never broke down. There's no water pump to break down. No fuel pump. No oil pump. There's no alternator, no starter motor or solenoid. No gaskets or hoses. No tune-ups. No oxygen sensors, no coils, no plugs. No catalytic converter. No timing belt. No positive crankcase ventilation valves. No carburetors or fuel injection nozzles. No idler pulleys. No push rods, rockers or valves... you get the idea. Trust me, I could go on for pages and pages. A typical gas engine has over a thousand moving parts that can, and eventually will, break down

2. Performance. There's no revving the engine up to 3000 RPMs just to get the torque you need. You can have full torque available starting at zero RPMs all the way up to highway speeds.

3. Maintainability. There's no radiator to check. No oil. No tune-ups. No timing adjustments. An electric motor has exactly one moving part — the rotor, plus two rotor bearings. That's it.

4. Clean. Never mind the environment. There's no messy leaks, no greasy engine, no exhaust fumes, no gasoline to refill. You get to keep your hands clean and breathe fresh air.

5. Quiet. Some people love the rumble and roar of a gas engine. But cruising along old country roads with the top down, the clean breeze in your hair and all the noise and rumble of riding a bicycle is a whole other kind of love you'll get to enjoy.

6. Oh yeah, it's also good for the environment. Study after study proves that in both the short term and over the lifetime of the vehicle, electric cars have a much smaller pollution footprint than gas cars. Plus, by resurrecting all the old steel and aluminum in the old car instead of consuming newly smelted and refined metals, you're being even more ecologically responsible than all those new-car EV people.

7. You will love your classic car even more than before, and people will be impressed. Sure, there will be some people who think you've ruined it. But there are also people who think we should still be riding horses. There's no doubt about it. Electric Vehicles are the future.

8. Everyone else will give you a hearty thumbs-up as you glide by in style, not polluting their world with noise or fumes.

And there are some downsides to making the switch:

1. Cost. Prepare yourself, it's going to be expensive up-front. But you will recover that money in the long run with lower fuel costs, lower maintenance costs and no more engine repairs. But it's not all that expensive. My TR3 project was still cheaper than buying a new car. And it transformed my classic car from an unreliable piece of garage candy into a confident daily driver. I actually gave my Toyota 4Runner to my daughter since I never drove it anymore. (I use my '59 VW bug for those days when it rains.)

2. Range. The twelve gallon gas tank could get me more than two-hundred and fifty miles between fill-ups. But I never drove that far in a day. In practice, I only had to fill it up every month or so. Imagine

having to visit a gas station every day! Not a pleasant chore. This is one reason why gas cars were given bigger tanks. It's so you don't have to fill-up as often.

But it's actually pretty rare for most people to drive more than forty miles in a day. My 20 kWh battery pack has a range of between 80 to 100 miles, depending on how I drive. And I can get more miles if I use one of the regeneration modes. I love that I never, ever have to visit a gas station. At the end of the day I just plug it in to any household electrical outlet to recharge overnight. If I need to recharge faster, I have a charging system that works off a standard 240 Volt 32 amp plug (like for clothes dryers or electric ovens) to charge about four times faster.

I could easily get more than 100 miles out of this battery pack if I pushed it harder, but I intentionally only charge it to 80% capacity and never deplete it below 30% capacity. This will keep the batteries healthy and extend their life to thousands of cycles. My batteries are rated for 4000 cycles. At one full-cycle per day, they'll last more than a decade. That's more life than most gas cars get. Since my commute is short, I only recharge it one or two times per week. In theory, my batteries will last longer than I will!

3. Resale-ability. A lot of people will balk at your DIY upgrade. But this is manageable. It all depends on how good of a job you do and the records you keep. One reason home-converted EV cars may lose resale value is because no one knows the credentials of the person who did the conversion, or whether the batteries have been abused, or how much life they've got left. Other buyers won't understand some of the specifics, like how many gallons is a kWh? How do kilowatts compare to horsepower? Where do I get service? Etc. This will all change as EVs become more common. If you document everything you do to the car — any modifications, wiring diagrams, brands, model numbers and serial numbers of components, dates of manufacture and company contact information, keep any invoices and any performance data and operational limits for the equipment, etc., and get a state-of-charge monitor that keeps a history of your battery, all that information increases the value of the car for the next buyer. And most importantly, do good, quality work. Neatness counts.

4. Innovation anxiety. Imagine spending $7000 on a new battery pack only to have it become obsolete a year later when someone introduces a new technology that's twice as powerful with half the weight, half the volume, and half the cost? That day is coming. By our best estimates, it won't happen until around 2030 or later, maybe much later. With technology innovation, you never know. Computing power tended to double every year while prices went down, but nuclear fusion power is supposed to be only a few years away, just like people have been saying every year for more than seventy years now.

5. Safety. It's no secret that modern cars are safer than older cars. But the raw statistical data for fatal car crashes seems to suggest a handful of things that can greatly reduce the chance of a deadly crash. Different sources showed different data, but the best I could glean from it all is this:

1. Don't speed. Obey all traffic laws. This is the number one reason for car crashes. It's that simple.

2. Don't drive in bad weather. Especially at night.

3. Don't be intoxicated or distracted. Obviously.

4. Drive like an adult. Teenagers are the most dangerous drivers. That's why they have such high insurance rates.

5. Drive like a girl. Most car fatal crashes are caused by male drivers—somewhere around 80% of them. Congratulations ladies. If anyone ever accuses you of being a "woman driver", thank them for the complement!

Seat belts were made mandatory in all cars starting in 1968, and airbags in 1998. Other safety improvements along the way include things like standardized bumper heights, crumple zones, automatic traction control and side-impact bracing. Of all these innovations, seat belts have probably saved the most lives of all, and lap belts are easy to install if your car doesn't already have them. It's something you should do. And learn to drive defensively. It can save your life.

The safety risks of driving an older vehicle are real, but they are manageable. All of life is a gamble. As the idiom goes, "You pays your money, and you takes your chances."

Therefore, and in conclusion:

For the vast majority of people (and for everyone else you share a planet with) the pros of converting your car to electric far outweigh the cons. The one and only reason I recommend for people NOT to do the conversion is because they simply don't have the skills or resources to do the conversion. If you do it right, you should be able to make your money back over time. But the payback isn't the real reason you're doing this. You're doing it because you love the car and want it to be seen, with you driving it.

There are an awful lot of people out there willing to plunk down more than a hundred grand for a well made replica of the Shelby Cobra—one of the fastest race cars ever made. For a fraction of that you can build an electric car that will leave the Cobra in your dust.

Let's get started...

Section Two:

Getting Technical

(Warning: May contain arithmetic. Not responsible for headaches.)

Choosing Your Car

If you already own a car you love and cherish and want to convert, go ahead and skip this chapter. Seriously, you can convert ANY gas powered car to EV. Of course, some cars are better candidates than others. It all depends on what's most important to you: Range, Speed, or Ease of Build. And of course, Cost.

If you're looking for a car to convert, the best thing you can get is a "rolling project." This is a car with a dead or missing engine but is otherwise complete. Be sure to inspect it for things like rust (especially on the frame underneath the car) or any damage. A non-running car typically sells for a fraction of what the same car would cost with a working engine. We're going to rip the engine out and replace it, so don't pay for it if you don't have to.

Aside from the condition of the engine, these are the main things to consider —

1. How much does the car weigh, including passengers and cargo, and what's the vehicle's gross weight capacity?

2. How much range do I need and where will the batteries go?

3. What kind of acceleration do I want?

4. Do I want or need air conditioning, power steering, power brakes, etc.

Let's address these one at a time.

1. How much does the car weigh, including cargo and passengers?

A lightweight car will be easier and cheaper to upgrade. The best option for cost, performance and thrill-factor is a small, two-seater sports car like an MG or Miata. Larger, heavier cars take more energy to get up to speed. It's a simple equation. The force you need (torque) is equal to the mass of the car multiplied by the acceleration you want. F=M*A. It's an equation every engineering student learns in their first semester.

In the glory years of the 1960s, zero to sixty miles per hour in twelve seconds was a thrilling acceleration! A lot of cars from this time could take half a minute to get up to sixty miles per hour, and that was considered normal.

Today, most trucks and SUVs can do it in about 12 seconds or less, and a sports car is more likely to be six or eight seconds, or less.

If your car is heavy (more than 3500 lbs.) you may need multiple motors to approach modern standards of acceleration, and you'll need bigger batteries to provide the additional amps needed to drive those motors. Basically, a bigger, heavier car can easily cost twice as much to convert as a small car.

But don't let that deter you. If you love the car (who doesn't love the Hudson Hornet?) and you don't plan to take 300 mile trips in it or drive it like an Indy race car, a larger, heavier car is still a reasonable project to consider.

2. How much range do I want?

This is another simple equation. More range = more cost. But it can get complicated real fast.

Batteries are the heaviest part of this project. The more batteries you install, the more weight you add. That means you'll want more powerful motors to accelerate all that mass. Then you'll need bigger batteries to push all the necessary amps for those motors, etc. etc. etc.

Here's the thing nobody wants to admit—A two-hundred mile range in an EV is like getting a jacked-up four-wheel drive truck to take the kids back and forth to school and buy groceries. Except for the rare few who actually drive more than forty miles a day and the few times a year you take a long trip somewhere, you just don't need more than about fifty or sixty miles of range.

Adding enough batteries to extend your range from 80 miles to 200+ miles can easily add ten to twenty thousand dollars to the cost of your project. Add too much weight and you'll need to upgrade the brakes and suspension too. And, some states won't register a car that's been modified to exceed the original load carrying capacity. Getting it approved to be street legal can be a tedious and iffy process.

Why pay for something like and go to all that trouble if you don't really need it? Having said that, we'll shoot for 80 miles of range. That's more than double what most people drive in a day, and the cost will still be reasonable. But the final number will be entirely up to you.

3. Where will the batteries go?

At the time of this writing, there are basically two types of batteries to consider— "prismatic" cell batteries that are rectangular and typically six to twelve inches high with terminals on top, and flat-pack battery modules like the Tesla and Leaf batteries that are typically three or four inches tall. The flat-pack batteries tend to be wide and long, around twelve to thirty inches, whereas the tall cell batteries are more customizable in width and length; you can even break them up into small chunks to distribute around various places in the car.

We'll go into more detail in the battery section of the book, so for now, just take an inventory of the spaces in your car where batteries can go.

Example: The VW Bug.

One of the more popular cars to convert is the classic VW bug. It is lightweight, robust and there are millions of them available in just about any condition you want to start from. They are not rare, so no one is going to be too upset if you gut one and modify it.

They have a convenient storage space behind the back seat where most people put as many batteries as will fit. The gas tank area under the front hood can hold a second set of batteries. This arrangement shifts the weight of the car forward, more toward the front wheels, which also improves the handling and safety of the car.

But there may be a better option. Most factory-made electric cars put the batteries under the floor, skateboard-style. They do this because it puts the center of weight of the car as low and as centered between the wheels as possible. Tesla uses a battery made of a massive array of 18650 battery cells. If you're not familiar with these, they are shaped like an oversized AA battery. 18650 literally means 18 cm high, 65 cm in diameter and 0 means cylindrical. The 18650 battery cell is a smidgen taller than two and a half inches. That's fortunate because one of the other great things about the VW beetle is all the upgrades and modifications available for it.

There is a pseudo lift-kit you can get to raise the body of the classic VW bug by 3 inches. It doesn't modify the suspension at all, so it's one of the easier lifts to install. With the body raised up you can put bigger tires on the car too — that's the "lift". A creative person could use this lift kit and put a second floor between the lift spacers and the car's body. This would provide a three-inch gap between the top and bottom floor-pans, a perfect space for a skateboard-style battery pack. Of course, there will be complications with the shifter and foot pedals, but that's just part of the challenge of building an electric car.

Another option would be to use any other kind of lift kit and sling the batteries underneath the original floor-pan, protected by a skid-plate. This is actually the approach I'll be taking with my VW bug project. You can do this with any car suitable for a "baja" or "safari" style upgrade.

Example: The Hudson Commodore

If you don't want to use the VW but still want the skateboard-style battery, there are classic cars from the 1950s with a "drop-down" floor to made sitting in the back seat more like sitting on a tall sofa than a modern car seat. The Hudson Commodore was one example of this. There were plenty of others, so you'll have to do your own homework.

These floors were characterized by a tall hump that ran the length of the car from front to back down the center of the floor. The hump contained the drive shaft. You could arrange a flat-pack battery on either side of this hump and construct a false-floor on top of the batteries. Plywood or aluminum plate would do the job to conceal them, and a little bit of carpet would hide the evidence. You'd sacrifice a little leg room in the back, but anyone accustomed to a modern car would never know it was missing.

Every now and then you can find one of these beauties in a restored condition. They typically sell for less money than you might think, and are dead-simple to work on. With a modern power plant and zero fear of break downs, they're a great investment — like a miniature living room on wheels.

Example: Pickup trucks

One of the simplest cars to convert is a small pickup truck like an older Toyota T100, Ford Ranger or Chevy Luv. The beauty of a truck is that you can put a small battery pack under the hood and stow a larger battery system in a "tool box" in the bed of the truck to augment the main battery. With a winch and a good design, you could even swap out battery boxes or double them up as needed for towing or for longer trips. You could even tow a trailer full of batteries, with solar panels on top and an emergency propane-fueled generator on board for extremely long trips.

If you don't want to sacrifice any of the pickup's bed, most trucks have a lot of dead space under the bed. You can make your battery boxes hang from either side of the frame, below the bed, and still be higher than the differential and front suspension.

Whatever car you choose, you're going to have to find space for the batteries, so get a tape measure and start hunting. A very rough estimate (based on LiFePO4 batteries) is between seven to nine miles of driving range for every cubic foot of batteries you install. (Note— this is a VERY rough estimate. It will depend on the weight of your car, how many motors you install, how fast you drive, other factors like air conditioning, heating, power features, lights at night, etc…)

You can put the batteries pretty-much anywhere, but keep in mind that they will be the bulk of the weight you are adding to the car. It is usually best to keep the weight distribution somewhere between 50/50 and 60/40, front-wheels to back-wheels, with slightly more weight on the front wheels.

4. What kind of acceleration do I want?

As we've already mentioned, weight matters. If your car is heavy you'll need more torque to accelerate it. To do this, you can add more motors, or use a shiftable transmission.

In the USA, fewer than 10% of people drive a stick shift (standard transmission). But in Europe, 80% of the cars are standard transmission. There are a lot of reasons for this. Standard transmissions are cheaper. People who drive them usually say they are more fun to drive — you have more control over the car, but conversely, you have to pay more attention to the car and the driving conditions. Until very recently, standard transmissions were more efficient than automatics. That's changed for modern cars, but not for the classics.

Technically, you can use an automatic transmission for your EV project, but it's a pretty bad idea. Gas engines are most efficient around 3000 to 5000 RPMs, so that's where most automatic transmissions are designed to shift. But that's not optimal for an electric motor.

Electric motors (generally) can supply torque even at zero RPMs and hit their peak efficiency around 5000 to 7000 RPMs. With an automatic transmission, it will always shift too early and miss the sweet-spot of efficiency. That means you won't get the range you could be getting. Plus, unless its a very new car, the automatic transmission is going to rob you of mechanical energy too, hurting your range even more.

If you're stuck with a car that has an automatic transmission, or the idea of learning to drive a stick shift terrifies you, don't worry. We have a solution to both of these problems. A good electric motor can generate its full torque from zero to about 8000 RPMs. This means you can replace the transmission with a simple single-speed gearbox, but you'll have to decide between top acceleration and top speed. The good news is you can have a happy medium between the two and greatly simplify your build.

Rather than get into the nitty-gritty details now, let's save that for the motor and drivetrain chapter. The bottom line is, if you want BOTH a fast acceleration AND a high top speed, you will need a manual-shift transmission of some kind.

In most cases you can just leave it in either second or third gear and drive it like an automatic. If you need more torque, like going up a steep incline or just showing off by racing away from a stop light, use second gear for that. If you'll be driving on the highway, use third. And if you really want to push your luck screaming down the straightaway at a hundred and ten miles per hour, just shift into fourth and hang on.

In all these cases you don't even need to shift on the fly. Since you have full torque at zero RPMs, you can start from a dead stop in any of these gears. The advantage to this is that you can get rid of the clutch too, further simplifying your conversion.

Having said that, there are advantages to keeping the clutch. I removed my clutch and I don't regret it. You'll have to make your own decision. We'll cover this in more detail later.

5. Do I want (or need) air conditioning, power steering, power brakes, etc.

The short answer is "no." Not yet anyway. Here's why: Converting a car to EV is actually a pretty big project. First let's worry about making it go. The air conditioning, power *this, that* and the *other things* are just going to add complexity. The components on a gas engine aren't right for an electric motor anyway. A gas engine keeps turning even when you're idling. Electric motors don't. That means no power steering, no air conditioning and no power brakes when the car isn't moving. Typically, that's when you need power steering the most (parking) and when your foot is on the brake (stop lights).

We can add those things later, after the main project of conversion is done. There are several after-market options for electrically operated air conditioners, power steering, brake boosters, vacuum pumps and the rest. They're usually simpler (no belts snaking their way around the front of your engine) and they work just as well. You'll also have the flexibility of putting one or more A/C units wherever they fit best — in the trunk, on the roof, under the hood... Wherever you want to put it.

And, you know how the A/C in your gas car isn't available while the engine is turned off for refueling on those hot summer days? Yeah, forget that. It's not an issue anymore. You can use the A/C anytime you want, whether the car is running or not. You know that annoying way your radio has to re-boot whenever you re-start the ignition on a gas car? Not anymore. Electric components operate independently of the engine.

Prep Your Space
Make A Plan

Two specific tools will be essential. These tools will save you time, eliminate frustration and make your project smooth, efficient and a pleasure to work on. And the best part is, they don't cost anything. In fact, having them will save you time and maybe even money. What are these tools? Space and organization.

You should clear enough space to work on this project. About the size of a two-car garage is best, with only the one car in it, preferably in the center. Around this car will be a work table, a place to store things like the old gas engine, the transmission, the new motor, pallets of batteries, boxes of wires, electronics, nuts, bolts, raw aluminum stock and a number of other things.

Having said that, I did my first project in a one-car garage. It was frustrating, uncomfortable and discouraging. I believe it cost me a few months of time. Even though the car was tiny (only five feet by eleven feet) I also had an 18" deep shelf system lining one long wall and another one on the short wall at the end of the garage. Every day I had to roll the car out into the driveway, erect an easy-up for shade and use the empty garage as my workspace. At the end of the day, I'd make room for the car and roll it back in for the night.

Another reason you will need space and organization is because there will be a lot of things to disconnect and remove when you take out the old engine. Save them. Label them. Keep them in order. A lot of it can be useful later.

Other Tools—
You will probably need some tools you don't have. Get them. It's a simple rule. Henry Ford said, "If you need a tool, buy it. If you don't you'll pay for it anyway." You really don't want to pay for it with lost skin or a crushed hand.

Of course, we're not all made of money. You have to be sensible too. Borrow if you can, but if you can't, my own personal strategy is this—if it's a tool I know I'm going to use many times over the course of many years, I spend as much as I can afford, maybe even a little more, to get the best quality tool I can. Going cheap on a tool usually means replacing it sooner or later. I'd rather spend double on a good tool once than suffer a cheap tool I'll have to replace two or three times.

But if it's a tool I will only ever use once or twice, like an engine hoist for a one-time project, then I buy the cheapest one that will safely do the job. But be careful. It's never worthwhile to skimp on a tool if the result is a hospital bill. Look around your shop and think about the task ahead. Over the weeks and months, you will do these things:

STEP ONE:

Gut the car.
- Drain and remove the radiator.
- Drain the gas and remove the fuel line.
- Remove the exhaust pipe.
- Remove the gas tank.
- Remove the battery.
- Remove anything else that won't be necessary or that might get in the way. I removed the horns, the steering column, the hood and the whole front-end of the body. This made removing the engine easier and provided better access to the frame. This will help when designing a new motor mount, battery storage system and wire paths.

If you have air conditioning, an oil cooler, power steering reservoir, etc. remove all that too. Keep it for now. You might be able to use some of this later. If not, there are electric versions of these for a lot of cars.

Obviously, you'll need to remove the engine. Refer to your owner's manual or repair manual for this. Be careful. Engines are heavy.

In most cases, you'll remove the transmission along with the engine. This is fine. It will make mating the electric motor to the transmission easier if it's outside of the car. For something like one of the air-cooled VWs, Corvair or another transaxle car, you can leave the transaxle installed.

Clean out and clean up the engine bay and anything you plan to re-sell or re-install into the car.

Weigh everything you removed that will not be re-installed and write it down. You'll need to add up these weights. The gas tank should have been empty, but in practice, it would be full of fuel. We need to add the weight of the fuel too—typically seven pounds per gallon. Multiply the capacity of the gas tank by seven. (12 gallons of gas, times 7 = 84 lbs., this is the weight of fuel.) Add that to your total.

Now you have a **target weight** for batteries, motor, controller and everything else. For a short range car, this is probably good enough. But you might want more. If that's the case, do this—

Look-up the GVWR (Gross Vehicle Weight Rating) of your car. This is the MAXIMUM CAPACITY of the suspension and frame of your car.

Now, look-up the curb weight of your car (sometimes it's called the shipping weight) and subtract that number from the GVWR. If the GVWR is 2800 lbs. and the curb weight is 2200 lbs. then your load capacity is 2800 - 2200 = 600 lbs. (just enough for two large adults and some luggage.) Let's call this number the **load capacity**.

But remember— we removed a lot of stuff that was part of the curb weight. Add the **target weight** you calculated earlier to the **load capacity** we just figured. If we removed 400 lbs of engine, gas tank and fuel, etc. (the target weight), then our new load capacity is 600 + 400 = 1000 lbs. This is the absolute maximum number of pounds you can add in motor, batteries and other things.

Of course, if you max-out your capacity with batteries, you won't have enough left for the weight of a driver, passengers or groceries, so be sure to include these in your calculations too.

Now— If you still want more weight capacity, you'll need to upgrade your suspension and brakes and maybe stiffen the frame. Some states won't license a car that's over the manufacturer's GVWR, so you may have to move to another state too. In general, it's not a good idea to go over the GVWR capacity.

STEP TWO:

Make a list of things to buy. Don't worry, we're not committing to anything yet. This is just a checklist. But it helps to do it in this order.

1. MOTOR
Once you decide on a motor, make a note of its size, voltage and how much it weighs. Refer to the chapter on motors to help you decide. The voltage you're using will be determined by which motor you buy. Choose a motor for the performance you want. Saving a few dollars on a lower powered system is probably not worth it.

2. CONTROLLER
This will be determined by the motor. Again, make a note of its dimensions and weight.

3. BATTERIES
Now that you know the voltage and amps you need, the weight capacity you have available, and the spaces they will go into, you can start to design a battery pack. Refer the the chapter on batteries for more info.

4. CHARGER
Choose one based on the final voltage of your battery pack, of course, but also on how you plan to use this car. If you plan to take long trips, you'll want a fast charger. But if you only want to commute back and forth to work and make the occasional grocery store run, then you can get away with a slower , cheaper overnight charger.

5. BMS, CC, SOC — Battery Management System, Charge Controller and State Of Charge monitor. These are small, but critical, components to your system. It will control the charging cycle, keep your battery cells balanced and let you know how much range you have. Don't skimp. They need to talk to each other too, so it's best to stick with one brand, or an integrated system.

6. WIRES. HEAT-SHRINK TUBING, LABELER. You're going to need to design and make a box to hold your batteries, so reserve a space in your garage for some metal work. If you don't have metal-working tools, aluminum is soft enough that you can use wood-working tools on it. That's what I did. Then just bolt it together instead of welding. This will make the design a little more challenging — you don't want bolt heads or nuts digging into your batteries — and aluminum costs more than steel. But it is light weight and it doesn't rust, so you won't need to pain it. Just leave it bare for a nice, sleek look.

Be sure to wear a face shield when using power tools on aluminum. The splinters can be razor sharp and tend to fly everywhere. Also, they're not magnetic, so you'll have to sweep them up the old fashioned way. A magnetic sweep won't work.

7. COUPLER/ADAPTER PLATE — I saved this one for last because it can be one of the more challenging things to find, and it's the most variable item too. You might not even need it.

There are several options (which we'll cover in detail later). But if you're able to use one of the ready-made adapters and connectors available for certain cars, budget at least $400 and as much as $2000 for this part. For VWs with the rear engines, there are even custom two-speed transaxles available for around $4000 or so. But before you decide, read the chapter about coupling the motor.

Motors and Controllers

Before you can buy batteries, you need to know how much power and what voltage your motor requires. The motor you choose will depend on the weight of your car and your intended driving style. At the time of this writing, the two most popular brands of motor are Netgain and HPEVS.

There are plenty of other options, including buying a junked older EV and recovering the motor and other items, or finding used electric motors from forklifts on Ebay and other on-line resources. If you take this route you'll be faced with the challenge of finding a matching controller. This is do-able, it's cheaper, and many people have done it. A lot of them have even designed and built their own controllers. But that kind of electrical engineering is beyond the scope of this book.

It's the old engineering optimization problem. You can do it cheaper, but the effort will be harder and the quality will suffer. If you want to take a quicker, easier approach, it will cost more. But don't forget — there's value in saving time and frustration too. Depending on how much your time is worth or how big of a learning curve you want to climb, the more expensive motor and controller might be the better value after all.

This book is intended for the 'weekend warrior' class of DIYers, so we're going to keep it as simple as possible. For this reason, I'd recommend sticking with either of the HPEVS or Netgain systems. They have integrated controllers and are very easy to configure. Of course, this is a changing landscape. Please do your own research! By the time this book is published there may be other, and possibly better options.

HPEVS stands for High Performance Electric Vehicle Systems. Their three most popular models are the 35, the 50 and the 51. Netgain's most popular models are the Warp-9, Hyper-9 and Hyper-9 HV.
Their web sites are: www.HPEVS.com —and— www.Go-EV.com

Other options:
At the most basic level, there are two kinds of motors — DC motors and AC Motors. A lot of people think that because the batteries are DC, they have to get a DC motor too. This is not true. It all depends on the controller you use.

The quickest way to tell an AC Motor from a DC motor is from the number of power terminals on it. This isn't universally reliable, but in the vast majority of cases it is. DC motors have two power terminals; positive and negative. AC Motors typically have three (most AC motors are three-phase. There are single-phase motors too, but these are less common for EVs.) Since each terminal on an AC motor is both positive and negative, the three contacts are usually denoted as U, V and W.

How do you connect three motor terminals to the battery's two poles? You don't. The controller (sometimes called an inverter) converts the DC from the batteries to AC for the motor.

Used Motors:

You'll need to decide whether to use an AC or DC motor. Each has its pros and cons. Older conversions almost always used DC motors. These days most people prefer AC motors. AC is a little more expensive and a little more complicated, but they require less maintenance and have more capabilities, like power regeneration and switchable forward/reverse (you can't do that with DC motors).

You should know there are many, many sub-types of motors within these two broad categories. We'll touch on a little of that in the paragraphs ahead.

DC motors have brushes that need to be replaced periodically. They are slightly less efficient than AC motors and cannot run in reverse mode or do regenerative braking. But they can be a lot cheaper — both for the motor and the controller.

AC motors are more efficient, can run backwards and do regenerative braking. Since they don't use brushes, they require no maintenance. But they are more expensive and are slightly more complicated to configure.

As far as power is concerned, either can give you all the torque you need (just be sure to check the spec sheet.) All the major car companies use AC motors and controllers in their production EVs. There's probably a very good reason for that. Unless you have a very good reason to use a DC motor, stick with the AC systems.

A quick review of Single Phase and Three Phase:

Single Phase looks like this:

With two electrical poles (positive and negative) there can only be one gap (phase) between them. The line represents a voltage gap between the two poles.

Three-phase typically looks like this:

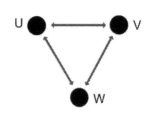

This is why you never hear of two-phase systems. With three poles, there are exactly three gaps (phases) between them. Each "pole" alternates between positive and negative at different times. The timing between these alternations is what forces the magnets inside the motor to turn the rotor to follow the magnetic flux around a circle. By managing the speed of those polarity flips, the controller manages the speed of the motor.

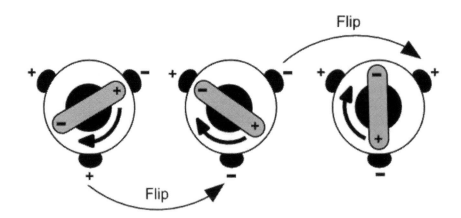

In the diagram above, V is negative while U and W are positive. The magnet aligns this way because opposite poles attract. Now, if W suddenly flips polarity, the magnet will be forced to turn 30 degrees clockwise. Next V flips for another 30 degrees, then U, etc... Each flip forces the rotor to turn 30 degrees.

In a modern motor there would be multiple instances of each pole so the rotor only has to turn a few degrees on each flip. Like this:

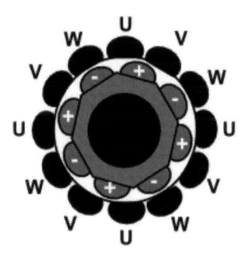

Different kinds of three-phase AC motors:

There are many types of three-phase motors. The main difference is whether it's an induction motor (think electro-magnets) or it uses permanent magnets in the rotor. At the time of this writing, the most powerful and most efficient motor with the widest torque band is known as a Synchronous Reluctance Permanent Magnet motor. These motors use a highly-engineered, shaped magnetic field to increase the torque. (If you want to know more about shaped magnetic fields, look-up a "Halbach Magnetic Array" for a simple introduction)

The Encoder:

For the controller to manage the timing of polarity flips effectively, it needs to know the position of the rotor inside the motor case. This is measured by something called a Hall Effect sensor. The sensors detect changes in the magnetic field inside the motor housing and send a signal to the controller. The encoder is usually at the base of the motor and will have connections for signal wires that need to go to the controller.

The signal wires must be shielded, and should take a different path to the controller than the power wires. A powerful electric current in a wire can induce a current in an improperly shielded adjacent wire. Without a clean signal, the controller cannot manage the motor effectively.

High or Low Voltage?

A lot of motors and controllers have options for different voltages. Common options are 48 volts, 72 volts, 144 volts, 288 volts or higher. In general, lower voltages are cheaper and less dangerous to work with. Higher voltages can give you more power. (This is not *technically* accurate. Power is independent of voltage. But it is *practically* true. Low voltages require higher amps to get the same power, and amps are harder to manage and more dangerous than volts. Amps are what tend to cause fires and kill people. By keeping the amps lower and volts higher, you can push a lot more watts down the same size wires.) Some factory made EVs operate at 700 volts or more. But those are designed and assembled by people with high-voltage electrical engineering skills that you probably don't have.

Why this is important: Gas engines are rated in horsepower. Electric motors are rated in kiloWatts. A kiloWatt is a thousand Watts, and a Watt is basically the Voltage multiplied by the Amps (current) being consumed. Remember this: Volts x Amps = Watts. Voltage is like the pressure of the water behind your spigot. Amperage is like the diameter of the spigot's opening. A higher pressure (higher voltage) system will deliver the water faster through the same size pipe. A low pressure system requires a fatter pipe to get the same quantity of water in the same amount of time. The size of the pipe is like the gauge of wire needed to carry the electrical current.

To get a certain number of Watts, a 72 Volt system will require twice as many Amps as a 144 Volt system. 15 kiloWatts divided by 144 Volts = 104 Amps. 15 kiloWatts divided by 72 volts = 208 Amps.

More Amps requires a thicker wire. More Volts only requires a better insulated wire. Higher voltage wires tend to be cheaper than higher amperage wires because plastic insulation is a lot cheaper than copper. Thinner wires are also easier to work with. Weighing all the pros and cons, it's better to go with higher voltages if you can do it safely. You'll spend a little more on the motor and controller, but you'll save money and frustration on the wires, fuses and connectors.

Speaking of wires — don't guess. Ask an electrician or *learn how to read wire gauge charts* to determine what size wire you need for your amp load, your voltage, and the length of the run. Then think about adding a safety margin to that. I would add a wire gauge chart here, but I'm not the manufacturer, and I've seen differences in the gauge charts from different manufacturers. I'm not sure why, and I'm not qualified to second-guess them, so please do your own homework. You don't want your car catching fire while going down the freeway, or worse, while recharging in your garage as you sleep.

You'll save a little money going with a lower voltage system, but not much. At the time of this writing, the sweet spot in the trade-offs between power, cost, workability and availability of parts for the DIYer all intersect around 144 volts. That's what I would recommend to a friend, but it's your decision.

The Controller

At its most basic level, your motor will need a controller than can take input from your throttle (accelerator pedal) and manage the motor's speed and power. But your controller will do far more than just control the speed. It can make your motor run in reverse, do regenerative braking, connect to a CAN bus (an automotive analog to ethernet) to send information to a display and other things.

The controller takes DC power from the batteries and modifies the polarity, voltage, amps, and phase of the current before delivering it to the motor. The controller also takes signals from your throttle and any switches you have wired into it, such as forward/reverse, regeneration high/low/off/variable, traction on/off, etc. plus any programming or configuration to alter its behavior based on certain conditions. In short, it is the computer that controls your drive system.

Don't be intimidated by all that. Netgain and Curtis controllers come with very good documentation. If you can follow a wiring diagram you shouldn't have much trouble. The most important thing is, you have to get a controller that is matched to your motor.

Wiring the motor and controller:

The motor will have three terminal lugs and a data connector (the encoder). The terminal lugs are typically labelled U, V and W. Just connect these with your high-power, high-voltage wires to the same terminals on the controller. U to U, V to V, and W to W.

Be sure to use the right gauge wire. Too many amps going through a wire that's too thin will do two things — it will limit the performance of your motor, and it can get hot enough to melt things and start fires. Buy a wire that's rated for the maximum amps your controller will pull from your batteries. I used 0/2 gauge welding cable and matching compression lugs. Keep the wires as short as possible while leaving enough slack for adjustments. (They should all be the same length too.) I used colored heat-shrink wrap to keep them organized. White for W, Violet for V (blue is close enough to violet, right?), and Yellow for U (think 'uellow').

My kids complained that the Violet shrink wrap is actually blue, and Yellow doesn't even have a U in it. Close enough. It makes sense to me. You do whatever makes sense to you. Use a label maker, or some other kind of system if you prefer. The important thing is to connect them to the right terminals.

The motor-end of the data connector is a little more problematic. For the Netgain controller I had to assemble the connector. With the right crimping tool and their handy PDF manual it was a pretty straightforward project that took about half an hour.

Wiring the controller and the battery — The Contactor:

To switch a high-power supply on and off requires something called a contactor. This is a sealed, electromagnetically activated, high-power switch. To prevent arcing or power surges, the contactor should have a "pre-charge" wire connecting it to the pre-charge terminal on the controller. Refer to the wiring diagram later in this book for more information.

Summary:

You have a lot of options in how you configure your system. The more you understand about how things work and how they connect together, the better your decisions will be. Read the documentations!

Batteries

Let's start with safety. NEVER FORGET— These batteries contain enough chemical energy to hurl a 2000 lb. car several *miles*. Imagine what they'll do to your heart if the full charge pulses through one of your hands, up your arm, into your chest and down the other arm to where your other hand is grounded. Always be aware of where the leads are and keep one hand behind your back when touching potentially charged surfaces. At these voltages and wattages, DC current can be more dangerous than household AC current. ***Take precautions.***

Batteries vs. Cells

A *battery* is not the same as a *cell*. Batteries are made from multiple cells. Most cell chemistries can only generate a low voltage no matter how big the cells is. For lead-acid, it's around 2 volts. A 12-volt lead-acid battery will have six cells, usually connected together in the same battery case. For Lithium Ion chemistries, it's around 3.2 or 3.5 volts per cell, depending on the cell's internal geometry. Larger cells can contain more total energy, but not a higher voltage.

To get higher voltages, you have to connect multiple cells into a "battery" of cells. The word *Battery* originally meant multiple hits, as in assault and battery, or a battery of gunfire. In modern usage it's a number of individual units merged together as a single unit.

We're going to make our own battery out of cells, so first we need to learn about the cells. There are basically two types of cells: *prismatic* and *cylindrical*.

Prismatic means the cells are rectangular, like a box. These are easier to stack into tight spaces and they tend to have screw-terminals for connecting to lugs and bus bars.

Cylindrical means exactly what you think. These are like AA, C and D cells, or the 18650 cells used in many laptop computers, high-end electronics and of course, Tesla's cars. Instead of screw-type terminals, these have a bare plate on top and bottom of the cells. They need a custom-made connector for most applications, or they can be welded into place.

Chemistry

There are a lot of different chemistries for batteries: Lead Acid, Sealed Lead Acid (SLA), Nickel Metal Hydride (NMH), Nickel Cadmium, etc. I could waste a lot of paper and ink on them. but there's no point. In a few years the technology will change anyway. For now, there is only one good choice for DIY EVs.

The best chemistry is currently the Lithium Iron Phosphate, or LiFePO4 battery cell. For size, cost, weight and power, LiFePO4 hits the sweet spot better than anything else. They typically come in 3.2 to 3.5 volt cells and a myriad of different sizes and capacities.

About 18650 Cells

The most popular cell in the world is the 18650 cell. These are used in everything from flashlights, laptop computers, power tools, solar power storage banks and even Tesla's cars. The name describes its shape — 18mm in diameter, 65mm tall. The 0 indicates it's a cylindrical cell.

The compact size of these cells make them perfect for "skateboard" style battery packs under the floor of the car. They have the advantage of being short — less than three inches tall. They also are widely mass-produced. Because of this, they can have a lower price per kWh than prismatic cells when purchased in bulk.

But they are not easy to work with. Because they are small and hold a limited amount of energy, large arrays of 18650 cells have to be spot-welded onto a conducting substrate to form a module of parallel cells, then multiple modules are connected to form the final battery. Since each cell only holds about 3 amp-hours of energy and can only produce a dozen or so watts, it takes a *lot* of them to power a car.

A Tesla uses more than 7000 (seven thousand!) of the 18650 cells. But with all these cells welded together, what happens when one of them goes bad and becomes a short circuit that wants to drain all the other cells in the module?

To accommodate bad cells, Tesla's modules have special fuses welded to each and every cell in the battery. If a cell goes bad and short-circuits, its fuse will blow and disconnect that individual cell from the pack, permanently. There's no way to replace it without taking a chunk of the car apart and doing surgery on the battery module, and that's probably not worth doing to replace a $5 part you can easily do without.

Since these cells are so robust and so many products use them, there are a plenty that still have a lot of useful life left in them in discarded laptops and power tools. You can find plenty of YouTube videos of people recycling these cells, usually to build solar power storage banks. With a little research you can find off-the-shelf products to make the job easier — things like like spacer grids, conductor plates, the fuses and the specialized welder and other tools to put it all together. It's not a bad option if you're willing to do the work.

Prismatic Cells

If you don't want to go to the trouble of welding a few thousand cells together, there's a much easier way, and at the retail level of purchasing power, it can even be cheaper than cylindrical cells. These are the rectangular cells, also called "prismatic" cells.

You can't use these for a skateboard-style battery. They tend to be tall, and it's a bad idea to lay prismatic cells on their sides. They typically have a vent valve on top. If you lay them over, they could potentially leak electrolytes and ruin the battery and your car.

A single prismatic cell can hold anywhere from about 20 amp-hours to 300 amp-hours, so you won't need as many. To figure out how many we need and what size we need, we'll have to do a little bit of simple math.

Sizing Your Pack

If your motor is designed for 144 volts, then you'll need to connect 45 of the 3.2 volt cells in series to get to 144 volts. (45 times 3.2 = 144. Also, if you don't know how to connect batteries in series, we'll get to that later.)

But 3.2 is only the "nominal" voltage for these cells. In practice they can usually go up to 3.6 volts But don't rely on this until you confirm with your battery manufacturer what the actual recommended max voltage is for your cells. If we push them to the higher voltage, then 3.6 volts x 45 cells = 162 maximum volts.

But isn't the motor only rated for 144 volts?

Again, this is the "nominal" rating. It can probably go higher. The Netgain Hyper-9 HV motor is nominally 144 volts, but it can go up to 180 volts safely. Be sure to check the technical details of your motor before you push the voltage.

For 180 volts we can safely increase the cell count from 45 cells up to 50 cells. 3.6 volts x 50 cells = 180 volts. This is good. We just increased our range by more than 10%. Now that we know how many cells we need, what size cell should we get? In other words, how many amp-hours should each cell hold?

Suppose you want to get 100 miles of range. The general rule of thumb is that you'll get somewhere between 2 to 4 miles for every kWh of battery capacity. Of course, this can vary a lot. My TR3 gets a little more than 4 miles per kWh. It depends on the weight of the car, the tire inflation, how hard you accelerate and what speed you drive.

My TR3 weighs almost exactly 2000 lbs. With a 20 kWh pack I can get about 90 to 100 miles at an average speed of about 45 - 50 mph (I avoid the highway in favor of long, winding country roads.) That's a little more than 4.5 miles per kWh. Let's assume you're converting a VW bug (more air resistance) and drive less conservatively than I do. You might only get 4 miles per kWh. To get 100 miles of range in a classic VW bug, divide 100 (miles of range), by 4 (miles per kWh), to get 25 kWh needed. You need 25 kWh of battery capacity to go 100 miles.

Since kilo means "thousand", 25 kiloWatt-hours (kWh) is the same as 25,000 Watt-hours. Remember that: 25,000 Watt-hours.

(For a truck or van, you might only get 2 miles per kWh. In this case 100 miles will require a 50 kWh battery, or 50,000 Watt-hours.)

Now we can figure out how big each cell has to be. Remember, Watts are just volts multiplied by amps. W = V x A (for you electrical engineers out there, I know. I know. This isn't exactly true. But it's good enough for what we're doing here. For everyone else, if you're really interested, there are ample tutorials on YouTube describing everything you'd want to know about Watts of energy.)

Back to our project: Battery capacity is measured in amp-hours. To find the amp hours you need for each cell, divide the Watt-hours you want by the total pack voltage. We know we're going to have 180 maximum volts for our pack and we want 25,000 Watt-hours total capacity for our VW bug project.

Easy peasy. 25,000 divided by 180 = 138.89 amp-hours needed for each cell. Let's just round that up to 140. (Another way to calculate it is 25,000 Watt-hours divided by 50 cells = 500 Watt-hours per cell. Since each cell has a max voltage of 3.6 volts, 500 Watts divided by 3.6 = 139 amp-hours for each cell.)

Cool. Let's go shopping for cells.

Hey, look at this one — Xcell makes a big 277 amp-hour LiFePO4 cell. That's twice the capacity we need. Why not get 200 miles of range!?!?

Check the weight. It weighs 12.4 lbs. *per cell.* Fifty of them will weigh 620 pounds! Can the car handle it? This is why the GVWR (total weight capacity) of your car is so important. It's a limiting factor on how many batteries you can install and therefore how much range you can get. Don't forget we're also adding a 130 lb. motor, about 50 lbs. worth of electronics and wire, and you still need to carry passengers and luggage too.

Suppose you decide the car can handle the extra weight. Can your budget afford it? Do you really need that extra 100 miles of range?

Most people rarely travel more than 40 miles in a day, so as long as you plug it in at the end of every day, 100 miles is more than enough for a typical daily commute and grocery run vehicle. Let's stick to the plan for 100 miles of range in our first project. And honestly, increasing the battery banks at a later date is not that hard to do.

Ok, we still need 50 cells of 140 amp-hours each, at a nominal 3.2 volts, but that we can charge up to 3.6 volts. This will get us our 25 kWh battery pack.

Wait... can't we just use 25 of the 277 Ah Xcell cells? No, because 25 times 3.6 volts isn't enough volts. We need the right number of cells at the right size. There's no easy way around this. (Actually, there *are* ways around this, but they are not easy and they will add cost. High power voltage converters are available, and there are tricks you can do by combining parallel and series together, but it's a bad idea — we'll get into that in a few pages. Keep reading.)

Now we need to figure out what physical shape to arrange these cells into so they fit in the car. To do this you'll need to measure the space you have — be as exact as possible. Be sure to accommodate the dimensions of the box that will hold the cells and any mounting hardware. Think about how the wires will run. Think about airflow for air-cooled cells, or if you'll add any plumbing for a liquid cooled system.

If this is your first project, keep it simple. Air-cooling is fine for most cases — just leave about 1/8 of an inch between each cell for air flow. Aluminum transfers heat better than plastic, so the aluminum encased batteries should fare better than the plastic encased batteries.

Does the brand name matter?

It might. But it might not. A lot of brands are actually made in the same factories using the same methods and components. The only difference could be the label on the outside. Others are more tightly controlled. The business landscape changes from month to month, especially with Chinese made items, so you'll have to do your own research.

When picking out your batteries, try to stick with UL certified batteries if you can. I've been told they're less likely to catch fire. Of course, these will be more expensive, and the manufacturers of non-UL certified batteries will tell you theirs are just as safe. So caveat emptor.

CALB makes UL certified cells at 72, 100, 180 or 200 amp-hours each. Unfortunately, none of those are 140 amp-hours, which is what we need. 72 and 100 are too small, but can we use the 180s? They weigh 12.6 lbs each. That's 630 lbs. of batteries. They are heavier than the 277 amp-hour Xcell cells! Why?

The Xcell cells are not UL certified and don't have the thick plastic protective casing on them. But the plastic casing could also shorten the life of the cell. It insulates the cell, keeping in heat. Heat is bad for LiFePO4 cells.

For whatever reason, we decide 600 lbs of battery is too much. Also the CALB cells are eleven inches tall, and we just don't have that much headroom where the batteries will go.

Can we double-up the 72 amp-hour cells to get 144 amp-hours? They are only 4.2 lbs each, so 100 of them is 420 lbs. We just shaved off 200 lbs! And they're only 8.7 inches tall. It seems like a perfect solution. Can we do that or should we keep looking?

Technically, you can do this. But it's not a good idea. Keep reading to find out why.

Parallel, Series, and mixed (and the danger)

Sure, you probably already know the difference between series and parallel. But do you know the different ways to mix them, why you need to, and what pitfalls to avoid?

First, a simple review. These cells are in series:

In series, the voltages add up but the amps stay the same. If these are 2 volt cells, and each is one amp-hour, in series they become a 6-volt, one amp-hour battery.

And these are in parallel:

In parallel the amps add up but the voltage stays the same. In this case we have a 2-volt, three amp-hour battery.

For most cell chemistries you can create strings of cells in series to get the voltage you want, then hook those strings in parallel. Like this:

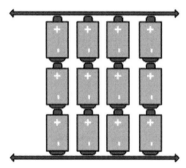

Here we have created a six-volt, four amp-hour battery out of cells that are rated at 2 volts and one amp-hour each.

BUT! — LiFePO4 battery chemistry works better the other way. They should be hooked up in parallel first, then the parallel strings connected in series. Like this:

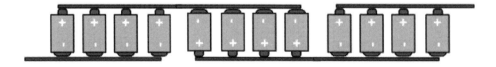

This battery is also four amp-hours and six volts. When you're buying cells and the battery management system, the nomenclature for this arrangement is 3s4p — three batteries in series, each made of four cells connected in parallel.

WARNING! DANGER!

Can you do this? Yes, you can.

Should you do this? Probably **NOT**.

Why?

When you connect Lithium Ion cells in parallel, then in series, you've created a river of electrons with multiple different paths. You will have eddy currents and surface charges that can force-charge some cells over their safe limits. Some cells will charge faster than others. Some will be slower. Some cells may become defective in time, then the other cells in that parallel string will be overworked, and that will cause the whole string to become defective in a cascade of failures, possibly resulting in a fire.

If you decide to create your batteries this way, you *must* include automatic cut-off fuses for each and every cell in the pack in the event of overcharging. The charge controller needs to be modified to accommodate the more complex arrangement, and the battery management system needs to know about it too. By doubling-up the cells in parallel you also double the complexity of the charging and balancing systems.

Also, you'll get less working capacity.

To prevent some cells from overcharging, the whole pack will need more headroom, which means you can't charge it to its full capacity.

The best thing to do is create a single string of cells connected in series *only*, using the largest cells necessary to get the range you want. Keep it simple. It's simply better that way. It might be a challenge to find the perfect cell, but it won't be as hard as all that extra wiring.

What is the C rating?

Imagine a jug of water. Something like a milk jug. It's full to the top. Now turn it upside down and count how many seconds it takes to empty. Logically, a larger hole will take fewer seconds. A smaller one will take longer. A vented jug will also empty faster than one that is not vented.

That's what the C rating for a battery is like. It's a measure of how fast you can dump the energy out. Basically, it's a ratio you use to calculate the maximum amps you can get from a cell.

Just in case it's not clear — Amps are different from Amp-hours. Amp-hours are a measure of total energy — the number of amps you can draw, and for how long. Whether you pull one amp for ten hours, or ten amps for one hour, or two amps for five hours, or five amps for two hours, is all the same. In each case you've pulled ten amp-hours of power.

To use the water analogy again, the amp-hours is like the total volume of water in the jug. The amount of water coming out multiplied by the time it takes to come out should give the same answer whether you pour a lot out fast or trickle it out slowly over a long time. The size of the stream of water at this instant is like the amps—a trickle, or a gusher, regardless of the size of the jug or how full it is.

Amps (without the hours) are measure of how much energy is flowing at an instant. How much power is available RIGHT NOW. Amps are like the size of the hole in the jug. How fast the water can escape is limited by the size of the hole. Different battery cells will have different C ratings depending on their internal geometry — the size of the "hole".

In practice there will be two C ratings for a cell. A surge rating (how much energy you can dump for a few seconds without damaging the cell — usually ten seconds or less). And there will be a standard rating (how much you can draw out continuously, until you run out of capacity.) To oversimplify, multiply the C rate by the amp-hour capacity to get the maximum *surge* amps you can pull from the cell. A 60 amp-hour cell with a C rating of 5 can provide 300 amps for your motor in short bursts. The constant draw C rating for most batteries is usually around 1 (one). A sixty amp-hour battery can usually supply 60 amps continuously. Sometimes more, sometimes less. You have to refer to the battery's technical specifications for details.

Why the C rate matters, a lot:

If your motor needs 200 amps of power for maximum torque, and your battery can only provide half that, then you'll never get the full performance of your motor and you'll wear out your batteries sooner. It's better to have stronger batteries (more available amps) than the motor needs.

Your motor will have a performance chart showing you the relationship between power, torque, amps, efficiency, etc. There doesn't seem to be a standardized format for these charts. I've seen them done all sorts of ways. You'll have to figure it out for your motor. But keep in mind, this is may represent a maximum load scenario.

At low speed on a straight, flat road your motor won't pull many amps. My TR3 pulls about 20 amps at 30 mph on a smooth, straight, flat road with no headwinds. At 60 mph it pulls 95 amps. And when I stomp on the accelerator from a dead stop it can pull 500 amps in short order. You need a battery than can provide that kind of current. Think of it this way. The motor pushes the car, but the batteries push the motor. Put your strongest player on the end of that chain. If you have excess battery capacity, it won't be wasted. It will translate into longer range.

Don't skimp on batteries!

Should you keep the transmission?

Coupling the motor to the transmission can be one of the most daunting tasks in replacing a gas engine with an electric motor. There are many ways to do it, some good and some not. It all depends on the specifics.

Direct drive — (If you have a transaxle instead of transmission, you can skip this section.) This is connecting your electric motor directly to the drive shaft. It is usually the easiest and cheapest way to install your motor. It can also be less efficient and less satisfying to drive. Electric motors run more efficiently at higher RPMs than gas engines, and by eliminating the transmission (and changing nothing else), you're guaranteeing that the electric engine will always run at a lower RPM than optimal. This will also make acceleration sluggish at best.

The only reason this works at all is because electric motors have so much torque at low RPMs. Still, without a gearbox you will have dismal acceleration compared to what is possible. Having said that, most people in normal driving situations rarely accelerate to sixty mph (100 kph) in less than ten or fifteen seconds. That's the best acceleration possible in most SUVs, the most popular type of car in America.

But you don't want SUV grade acceleration in a sports car. At least, not by today's standards. In the 1950s and early 1960's a lot of sports cars, like the Triumph TR3 and the MGA bragged about going from zero to sixty in only 11-12 seconds. Compared to Volkswagen's Kaman Ghia "sports" car, 11 seconds was indeed impressive. But we can do better than that.

The general rule of thumb about ditching the transmission and going direct drive is—don't. But there are some good exceptions to this rule you might want to consider. In practice, I almost never use anything other than second or third gear, and 80% of my driving (city streets) is in second gear. I could easily do without any other gears at all. In fact, the only time I use third gear is on the highway or if I ned to go more than 60 miles an hour.

If you do more highway driving and less city driving, you can leave in in third gear. My car has no trouble accelerating from a dead stop and driving exclusively in third gear. It's just slightly more sluggish than second gear. (But it still leaves my Toyota 4Runner in the dust.)

If you replace the transmission with a simple gearbox that replicates third gear, or somewhere between second and third, then you can probably ditch the transmission altogether. This is exactly what some of the EV conversion shops in Europe are doing. People already understand how to drive with an automatic transmissions and a one-speed car is pretty close to that experience.

For those who prefer to shift, you should know that it's different in an EV. You won't need to shift as often, and matching the RPMs of the motor is a lot harder. If you keep the transmission you'll have to find an adapter for it, or have a custom adapter designed and manufactured if your car is unusual. Or, if neither of those are in your budget, it's also possible to have a "virtual clutch." More on that further down.

First, let's do a little math. Don't worry, it's just simple arithmetic. We need to calculate the acceleration you'll get with direct drive (no gear box). All you need to know is the weight of the car, the radius of the tires (from center-to-tread), the gear ratio of the differential and the total torque of your electric motor at zero RPMs. If you have more than one motor, add their torques together. Here's a handy list with detailed explanations below:

1. Motor Torque (in Nm): _____

2. Tire radius (in meters): _____

3. Differential Gear Ratio: _____

4. Car mass (in kg): _____

1. The **torque of your motor** is probably supplied in Newton-meters. If not, let's convert them. Trust me, the final equation is much easier in metric units than Imperial units. We'll convert the final answer back to miles at the end. If your motor's torque is already in Newton-meters, skip this step. Otherwise,

   Torque in Nm = Ft-lbs x 1.356
   Some motors list their torque in Inch-lbs. In this case, **Nm = Inch-lbs x 0.113**

2. Measure the **RADIUS of your tires**. Measure the distance from the center of the tire to the tread. We need this number in meters, so,

   Meters = Inches divided by 39.4

3. Find the **gear ratio of your differential**. Sometimes this is stamped onto the differential case. It should also be in your owners manual (but it might not be, or they might list several if there were options for your specific kind of car.) And you can look it up on-line. If none of those work, you can measure it by lifting your rear tires off the ground, disconnecting the transmission from the drive shaft (you'll need to do this eventually anyway) and turning your drive-shaft by hand. Have someone count the revolutions of your tire while you spin the driveshaft exactly one rotation. Your answer will probably be something like 2.7 or 3.4 or so.

To get exact fractions, keep turning the drive shaft and count the rotations until you get both drive shaft and tire back to their original positions, then divide. For instance, if you turn the drive shaft five full rotations and the wheel goes around 17 exact turns until they're both in their starting positions, then 17 divided by 5 is equal to 3.4. The higher this number is (preferably somewhere between 5.0 and 7.0) the better your performance will be if you go with direct drive.

4. The **weight of your car**. As already mentioned, there are two weights for most cars, the Gross Vehicular Weight Rating (GVWR) and the curb weight or shipping weight. In this case, we need to know

the entire weight of the whole car including passengers. It's the curb weight, minus the stuff you took out (engine, gas tank, etc.), plus the stuff you added (motor, batteries, etc.), plus passengers. We need this number in kilograms. It's ok to make an educated guess, but the result will only be as good as your guess.

Kg = Weight in lbs. divided by 2.2

Now calculate the acceleration:

Here is one of the most fundamental and important equations in physics. And it's a simple one.

$$F = M*A$$

Force is equal to Mass times Acceleration.

We know the torque of the motor (force), and we know the mass of the car in kilograms, so let's calculate the acceleration. Force divided by Mass = Acceleration.

BUT FIRST we need to convert the torque of your motor into the torque (force) *between the tread and the pavement.* How much *push* does the tread put to the road? To do this, multiply the Torque (in Nm) times the gear ratio of your differential, then divide that by the radius of your tires.

EXAMPLE: A Torque of 220 Nm times a gear ratio of 3.7
220 x 3.7 = 814 Nm delivered to the axle.

814 Nm divided by 0.3 meters (radius of the tire)
814 / 0.3 = 2713.3 Newtons of **Force acting on the pavement to push the car.**

Now that you have the force, divide it by the mass of the car in kilograms to get the acceleration. This will be in physics format — meters per second per second. We'll covert that into a zero-to-sixty time next.

EXAMPLE: 2713 Newtons of force at the wheel, divided by 909 kilograms = 2.98 meters per second, per second. (If you're not familiar with acceleration, that's now much your speed will increase each second. After one second, you'll be going 2.98 meters per second. After two seconds, 5.96, after three, 8.94, etc… The mathematical notation is m/s^2)

To convert that into how many seconds it will take to go from zero to sixty mph, first we'll convert it to miles per hour, per second. There are 1609.34 meters in a mile and 3600 seconds in an hour. You can calculate the conversion for yourself if you want, or just multiply m/s by 2.2376 to get mph.

EXAMPLE: $2.98 \ m/s^2$ x 2.237 = 6.67 miles per hour, per second (mph/s).
Now, take 60 mph and divide by mph/s to get the seconds.
60 / 6.67 = 9 seconds (rounded).

(for you metric-minded people, multiply m/s^2 by 3.6 to get kph/s, then divide 100 by your calculated kph/s to get the seconds from zero to 100 kilometers per second.)

Nine seconds is not bad. But keep in mind, this is a *theoretical* number. It doesn't account for mechanical friction, rolling friction, air resistance, controller configuration, the C rate (discharge capability) of the batteries, etc, etc, etc. Your real world experience will be less. Probably a lot less. Nine *theoretical* seconds is probably more like 12 to 15 seconds in real life. Still about the same as most SUVs.

If only we could double the acceleration.

To do that we'd need to double the torque.

Fortunately, there is a thing called a "doubler" that does this.

A doubler is a super-simple one-speed transmission that you do not shift. They are also known as under-drives (the opposite of an overdrive) and are usually designed as some kind of planetary gear box. Doublers and under-drives are mostly used in rock-crawling trucks to reduce the RPMs and increase the torque for extreme off-roading. For us, it will be a small one speed transmission to replace the original.

There are two big advantages to this—it will take up a lot less space than the stock transmission. You might even be able to put your electric motor in the transmission tunnel and leave the entire engine bay for batteries — thus lowering the center of gravity, making the car safer, and potentially creating extra "frunk" space. Doublers are also lighter in weight and require less maintenance than a transmission.

Most doublers don't actually double the gear ratio. A lot of them have ratios of 2.77, or 3, or 5. That's probably too much for our needs. We're more likely to need a 1.5 or 1.8 ratio gearbox. But you'll need to do the math for your own situation. Just multiply the gear ratios in your drive train to get the total. A 2.77 ratio doubler connected to a 3.7 differential creates a 10.249 overall gear ratio. That's too much. Ideally you want it between 5 and 7, depending on the weight of your car, the power of your motor and your driving preferences.

Obviously, if you keep the transmission (assuming it is a standard trans) you have the option of using whatever gear you want for whatever conditions you're driving in. In my case, I didn't trust the math, so I kept the transmission. I'm glad I did. Fourth gear is usually a 1:1 gear ratio, so it's a good indicator of what direct drive will be like. It works, but it's not good. Third is better, and second gear is a lot better.

The downside to keeping the transmission is that connecting the motor to your trans is a lot more complicated, especially if you want to keep the clutch too. That's covered in the next chapter.

Connecting the motor to the drive-train

There are essentially four ways to connect your electric motor to the drive train. From easiest to hardest, they are:
1. Direct drive via a one-speed gearbox or straight to driveshaft
2. Attach motor to transmission, minus the clutch.
3. Attach motor to transmission and keep the flywheel and clutch.
4. Drive the rear axle or wheels directly by eliminating the differential or transaxle

Your electric motor will probably have a smooth shaft with a keyway cut into it. The shaft is typically designed for an interference fit. In other words, the hole in the coupler will be slightly too small to fit over the shaft. You'll have to heat up the coupler to expand the metal, then slide it on *while still hot* with a rectangular metal "key" in the keyway of the motor's shaft. Once it cools, the coupler is installed semi-permanently. It won't be easy to remove.

You can also get couplers that will slip on without being heated first. These are "slip-fit". But in this case, the 'key' is the only thing transferring power from the shaft to the coupler. It won't fail right away, but these are more likely to fail over time. An interference fit is better, and not difficult to install. I heated mine in an ordinary kitchen oven at 500 degrees for about 30 minutes. Then I used ordinary kitchen hot-pads to handle it. It was a lot easier than I expected.

Different kinds of couplers

One of the more popular types of couplers is the Jaw-type, or "spider" couplers made by Lovejoy and other manufacturers. They look like this:

These are semi-flexible couplers that are somewhat forgiving of less-than-exact alignments. At high RPMs, an out of alignment rigid connection can destroy a car transmission. The best thing about these couplers are that you can mix-and-match the pieces for your application. Each end can be specific to the kind of shaft it connects to. In my case I needed a coupler for a 1.125" keyed shaft on one end, and a 1.25" splined shaft on the other.

There are dozens of other types as well — chain couplers, nylon sleeve, universal joint yokes, and on and on. Search for flexible shaft couplers and be prepared to spend a day or two with the results.

The important thing is to get one that can handle the maximum torque AND the maximum RPMs your motor will generate.

Direct Drive (again)

As we've already discussed, the easiest way to connect your motor is to fit a yoke on it and connect it to the drive shaft just like the transmission did. Alternately, you can couple the motor to the one-speed gearbox you got, then connect the yoke to the gearbox. But there are good reasons why most people don't do this. Here are the other options.

Motor to Transmission (with clutch and flywheel removed)

When you get rid of the clutch, the transmission will probably have a splined shaft with a finger extending from the center of it. This finger is a problem. You probably won't find a coupler deep enough to fit the splines and also reach past the finger. You'll have to either cut the finger off (and ruin the main shaft of the transmission if you ever want to sell it or use it on a gas engine again), or, if you're feeling bold, you can fabricate your own extension for your coupler.

That's what I had to do. It took three very specific and hard-to-find adapters. Finding those adapters tool almost a month in itself. Fortunately they fit together perfectly. Still, I didn't just trust it. I tested the balance at high RPMs and verified it to be on-center within $1/1000^{th}$ of an inch. How did I do that? I used to do a lot of CNC work, so I have tools and techniques to test and measure these things. If you don't, then you should stick to whatever off-the-shelf couplers and adapter plates will work for you. High torque and high RPMs are nothing to play around with.

After all that, the face of my motor was 3.375 inches away from the bell-housing of the transmission. I had to craft a custom adapter plate and fabricate custom spacers between the motor and transmission. The hard part was getting the shafts lined up to each other, again, within $1/1000^{th}$ of an inch.

Somehow I managed to do it right. There's no vibration, no noises and no problems so far. But I wouldn't do it this way again. Next time, I'll sell the transmission and get a one-speed gearbox, then yoke that to the driveshaft. Or find a good two or three speed transmission I don't mind cutting-up.

Driving without a clutch

You can shift from a dead-stop into any gear and take off from there. But shifting on the fly is tricky without a clutch. You have to match the rpm of the engine with the rpm of the gear you're shifting into. You probably won't have a tachometer on your electric motor unless you opt for one of the more sophisticated displays. But there's a way to install a "virtual" clutch. the Netgain and Curtis controllers can be configured with a switch to put the motor in a zero-torque mode. This is different from just letting your foot off the throttle. If you have a regen mode on, that creates a negative torque when you lift your foot off the pedal. Some people like to program "forward creep" into the throttle mapping to mimic how a gas car works at idle while in gear. If you do that you'll have torque even with your foot off the throttle. A zero torque mode overrides all that.

I used a proximity switch connected to the clutch petal and a stiff spring. When I depress the clutch petal the zero torque mode is turned on and the motor goes limp, even if it is in one of the regen modes. The motor has more angular momentum than the old clutch plate did, so shifting takes a little bit longer. The synchro-mesh in the transmission is now taking on the job of the clutch. It will match the RPMs of the motor and transmission if you shift slowly. It's not a perfect solution, but it's a whole lot easier than trying to keep the original clutch and flywheel, especially since you rarely need to shift.

Having said that, if you find the right speed and right timing for your shift, you can do it just as fast as a conventional clutch. For me, shifting from second to third around 45 mph is smooth as silk. But to downshift I usually wait until I'm stopped. I don't really need any other shifting than that.

Motor to Flywheel with Clutch

This is a common installation in the professional shops. You'll need to find a custom adapter kit with matched flywheel hardware. CanEV.com is the best source. They make quite a few of them. You'll have to check their web site to see if they have one for your car. Follow the instructions that come with it.
You can also get CanEV's adapter kits through EVWest.com and several other on-line merchants.

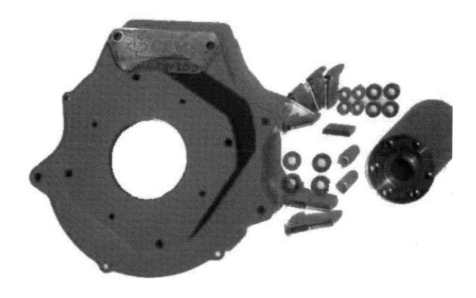

Rear Axle Installation

The old Nissan Leaf has a motor and gearbox that take the place of the differential on a traditional car. It's like a transaxle. There are two stub axles that come out of each side. If you have independent rear suspension, you may be able to install one of these into your rear-end. But this will require a lot more adaptation and fabrication that's beyond the scope of this book. Not recommended for beginners.

Motor-In-Wheel

The Aptera three-wheel car and some of the EV Motorcycles use in-wheel motors, also known as hub motors. In some cases you may be able to install these to your wheels. I used one to create a self-balancing motorized unicycle once. The motor is easy to work with. It's a three-phase AC motor with hall effect sensors, just like the others. But it's more compact and may not be quite as powerful. But then, you can put one on each wheel. Aptera puts them on all three wheels of their car.

Most hub motors have to be supported on both sides — they don't bolt-on to an axle like typical car wheels, so they're mainly used for motorcycles. But people have mated the rear end of a motorcycle to the front-end of a VW bug, dune-buggy style, so it's not out of the question!

The Charger, Charge Controller
and State of Charge Display

In normal operations, the worst thing you can do to a battery is drain it completely.
The second worse thing you can do is overcharge it.
You need a charging system that knows when to stop.

There are three parts to the charger:
1. The charging station on the wall that takes power from the grid/house and delivers it to the car.
2. The charger in your car that accepts AC current from the station and delivers DC to your battery.
3. The EVCC (Charge Controller) in your car that tells the charger what to do and when to stop.

And there's a fourth item to keep you informed about the amount of energy in your batteries — the SoC (State of Charge) display. It's not always part of the charging system, but it should be.

Charging Stations

First let's clear-up a little confusion about the charge adapter. Europe has a different standard charge adapter than Tesla, and Tesla has a different standard than just about everyone else in the USA, which is also different from Europe's standard. That may change one day, but for the moment, there's plenty of room for confusion. There are a lot of terms thrown around too: Level 1, Level 2, Fast Charger, SuperCharger, etc… Regardless of how it's named, what really matters is whether the plug is compatible and how many watts can it deliver to your car.

Tesla
"Supercharger"

J1772
(North America)

J1772 "Combo"

Mennekes
(Europe)

CHAdeMO
(older Nissan, Toyota, etc.)

GB/T
(China, parts of Asia)

I'm not going to try and second-guess how all that's going to evolve in the future. However it ends, there will probably be plenty of conversion adapters available, similar to those electrical outlet travel adapters for European plugs vs. American, Australian, etc. Or the various USB and 'Lightning' adapters, etc. So keep that in mind as you read this chapter. I'm going to focus on what seems to the the most common choices in the USA market for DIY EV conversion projects. At the time of this writing, that's the J1772 connector.

There are two flavors for this — the normal version shown here, and the "combo" version. The normal version is limited to 80 amps, but most retail level versions can only handle 32 amps, maxing out at about 7.5 kilowatts, or about 20 - 25 miles of range per hour of charge time, give or take.

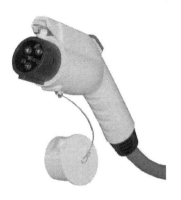

The combo version is not typical for at-home charing. It contains technology for dangerously high-voltage, high wattage charging. You'll need a special kind of charger installed in your car for this too.

It is possible to forego the special plug altogether and just use an ordinary extension cord. But that might not be a good idea. The J1772 plug contains safety features that prevent accidental discharge, and charging stations on the road will require them. Still, (in the humble opinion of this writer) if ordinary household plugs are good enough for most appliances, then why not your car too? Anyone can buy a generator with a 240 volt outlet, and most households have 240 volt plugs in the laundry room for the dryer. Your house almost certainly has 240 volts available in the breaker box. All you need is to have an electrician install a charging circuit for you, then you can use whichever of the multitude of off-the-shelf 240 volt plugs is suitable for your selected amperage.

If you still want the J1772 receptacle for charging on the road, portable chargers with wall-plug adapters are plentiful too. This is what I use. No special circuits needed. I can plug it in at home, or at a friend's or relative's house.

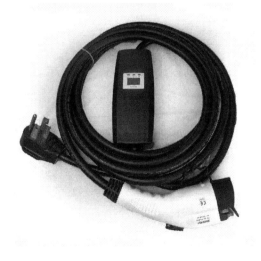

For overnight charging, a 110 volt household outlet typically supplies up to fifteen amps. This will give you a maximum of 1650 watts (110 volts x 15 amps = 1650 watts). Let's round this down to 1500 watts — we don't want to overheat any wires or blow any fuses. If you have a 20 kWh battery, it will take a little more than thirteen hours for a full recharge (20,000 watt-hours divided by 1500 watts = 13.3 hours.) But this will be rare. You don't typically run your car all the way to empty, especially when you park at a refueling station every night.

If your range is 80 miles on that battery, that comes to six miles for every hour of recharge. If you drive thirty miles each day, you can get a full recharge in five hours. This is a perfect scenario for simple, cheap overnight charging. If you want more, a 220 volt 30 amp circuits will supply four times the watts. That will give you 24 miles of range per hour of charging.

If you search for EV charging stations on-line, you'll find dozens of options ranging from a few hundred bucks to a few thousand. For some of the portable ones, you can adjust the voltage and amps depending on where you plug it in. Some are "smart" so they can make the adjustments themselves. The wall-mounted charging stations require an electrician to install it using code-approved wiring to your home's distribution panel.

Only you can decide which solution is right for you. I paid $400 for a "semi-smart" portable charging station that fits into my trunk. With a simple adapter I can plug it into any ordinary household plug for 13 amps at 110 volts. If that trips a breaker, it can be downrated to 10 or even 6 amps. It can also go up to 32 amps if I can find the right outlet for it. I call it "semi-smart" because it can automatically adapt to whatever voltage I give it, but I have to select the amps manually.

Other people I know opted for the permanently installed option. With two electric cars, they have a dual charging station mounted on a wall in their garage. I didn't like this solution because you can't charge at a friend's house or any hotel. When you're on the road you have to find a retail-grade charging station — and hope it works. One of my local legacy-brand car dealers has a J1772 charging station right in front of their sales office. It doesn't work. They seem to like it that way.

The downside to a portable charging station is having to haul the cord out of the trunk when I want to charge it. In practice I tend to leave it on a hook in the garage, then pack it in the trunk if I think I'll need it. So far, I've never needed it. I've always been able to charge overnight in the garage.

If you want the ability to recharge on the road in the USA, you need the J1772 plug or a Tesla adapter and access to their charging network, otherwise you can use any of the NEMA electrical outlet plugs suitable for your voltage and amperage needs. The only reason you might want to avoid the J1772 is cost. They are ridiculously expensive. But used ones are available in some markets at a fraction of the cost.

The Charger

For best results and the safety of your battery, be sure to get a quality charger and charge controller. It's best if you can get one that communicates and integrates with your BMS. At the time of this writing, the most popular brands are Thunderstruck and Orion. But that can change, and it probably will.

Since there are so many features and options and types of chargers in the rapidly changing world of EVs, you'll have to do your homework and find the charger that's right for you. (links to popular suppliers are listed near the end of this book) The important thing here is to get the right voltage and amps for your battery and your charging goals.

Measuring the voltage of your battery pack is easy, but it is *not* an accurate way to keep track of the state of charge. LiFePO4 batteries have a very shallow voltage variance though the middle 80% of their charge cycle. Here's a graph of the voltage changes for a LiFePO4 battery:

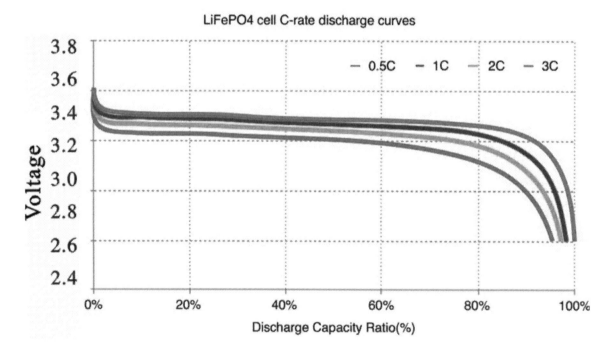

As the load on the batteries changes, their charging curves will also fluctuate. It can bounce from one of these curves to another and back again, making the state-of-charge impossible to judge by voltage alone. Aside from that, the charger is pretty simple. It just converts AC to DC and feeds it to the battery at a specified voltage and amperage profile. But to do this safely, you need something to manage the charger and tell it when to stop.

The Charge Controller

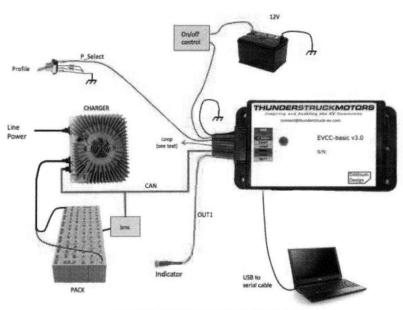

Figure 1 – EVCC-basic System Diagram

If you want to get the maximum life out of your battery, you need to have a charging profile that changes according to your battery state of charge, the size of your pack and even the temperature of the cells. The device that does this is the charge controller. How well it can do this job depends on how well it is integrated with the BMS and the capabilities of the BMS — not all of them can monitor the temperature. The Charge Controller will need to be programmed to adjust the amps being delivered to your batteries as the voltage rises to the target level.

Imagine driving your car toward a cliff. There's a guard rail to keep people safe, but everything has its limits. A car going too fast could still punch through it. When you're 10 miles away, you can go as fast as you want. When you're one mile away you should be slowing down. Clearly, the closer you get, the slower you want to go, or you'll suffer the consequences. The rate your charger pushes power into the batteries is like the speed of the car. If you overshoot and overcharge the batteries you could rupture the internal structure that keeps the electrons in place.

Since the voltage of the batteries stays flat for most of the charge cycle, it's a lot like driving in a fog on a long, straight road (for the sake of argument, assume you are the only car on the road and there are no animals.) If you really need to be somewhere soon, you can go as fast as you like. Visibility is short, but still good enough to stay between the lines. But how will you know when you're getting close to the edge of that cliff? You need a way to measure the distance remaining.

The old lead-acid batteries had a long, sweeping voltage curve as they charged. You could tell where you were in the charge cycle by the shape of the curve. There is still a curve at the end of the Lithium charge cycle, but it's short and sharp. If you want to charge fast (like driving fast in a fog), you need to know how close to the end you are. The best solution is something called a coulomb counter. It keeps track of how much electrical charge passes through a wire. By counting how much energy has been used, it knows how much needs to be to put back.

Shunts and Hall Effect sensors:

How do you measure the amount of energy passing through a wire? There are two simple ways to do it. And as usual, one is cheaper and less accurate, and one is more expensive and more accurate.

The cheaper option is called a shunt. A shunt is nothing more than a metal bar. But it's a very precisely manufactured bar that's tuned for a specific amount of amperage passing through it. The resistance of the bar is low, but very carefully calibrated. As electricity passes through it, the resistance causes the voltage to drop a tiny amount (and get converted to heat). By measuring that voltage drop it is possible to calculate the energy (watts) passing through the wire. As long as you stay below the amperage rating of the bar, it's a safe, inexpensive and effective tool. But there is a more accurate and more efficient method.

When electrons pass through a wire, they also induce a magnetic field around the wire. Likewise, when a magnetic field moves across a wire, it induces a current in that wire. By wrapping a very carefully designed and manufactured wire around our main wire, the changes in the magnetic field caused by the current can be measured. This is a donut-shaped sensor called a Hall Effect sensor.

Either of these will work. Most hobbyists tend to use shunts because they are so cheap and simple to use. In my opinion, the Hall Effect sensor is even easier to use, but it is definitely not as cheap. For my car a shunt would have been about $20. The Hall Effect sensor I bought was $80. But these only measure the current. They are analogous to the speedometer cable in your car. They can only transfer instantaneous information. You still need the counter.

The coulomb counter is a small computer — often it is part of the SOC (State of Charge) display, your EVs "gas gauge". You can get a relatively inexpensive version that displays the empty/full status of your battery pack, or you ca get one that does a lot more.

I chose one that can display the status of each individual cell as well. It also shows me the instantaneous voltage and amperage my motor is using (I find this useful for judging my driving efficiency — I can adjust speed and acceleration for different driving conditions. Hills, headwinds, even extra people in the car make a difference I'd never have known about without the display.) It also talks to the Battery Management System and the Charge Controller. I can manage both of those and change settings from the display in the dashboard.

The bottom line is this — if you want the simplest possible solution, your charger needs to cut-off when you reach your target voltage. If you want to maximize the life of your battery, you'll need to adjust the amps going into your battery depending on their temperature and state of charge. This requires a BMS, Charge Controller and Charger that all speak the same language and can communicate with each other. It's best to stick with one brand and buy an integrated system. Some vendors will even pre-configure them if you tell them your battery's chemistry, size and structure.

The CAN bus:

If you're wondering how these components communicate with each other, they use a two-wire network protocol called C-A-N. CAN stands for Controller Area Network. It's kind-of like an internet for all the electrical components of your car.

Why do you need it? It simplifies the construction and repairability of the car. Instead of having individual wires running between every device and the dashboard controls, All you need is two wires. The controls/switches drop instructions on the CAN bus, then each device listens for its unique instruction code. Turn the AC on, adjust the wiper speed, roll down the rear window… everything can be controlled with just two wires this way.

That's the theory, anyway. In practice it also adds complexity and makes the whole car vulnerable to a single point of failure. If the bus goes down — broken wire, or rogue controller that floods it with high-priority instructions, well, good luck.

Personally, for things like wipers and lights and window motors and even AC units I think the regular wiring is preferable, but for complex communications, like the Charger, BMS, Charge Controller and SoC display all require, a CAN bus is absolutely the best way to do it. And it's super-simple. Just two wires connect all that.

And you can have more than one CAN bus. It would be prudent to use one CAN bus for your high-voltage components and a separate one (if you even need it) for 12-volt things like the AC and heating controls, wipers, lights and such.

The SoC (State of Charge) Display:

The simplest version for the SoC display is nothing more than a digital gauge that replaces the fuel gauge in your car's dashboard. If you want to use the original fuel gauge, all you need is an SoC that can mimic the sending unit of a gas tank. Most of the higher-end devices can do this.

A more sophisticated SoC will tell you the health and history of every cell in your pack. This is not generally useful, but it will save you a lot of troubleshooting and can give you advance warning if one or two cells in your pack start to go bad.

Whatever you get, it will need to be compatible with your charging system. This will limit the choices you have. It is best to stick with the same manufacturer for all these things, with the exception of the DC-DC converter (more on that in a later chapter).

If your controller and charging system are compatible with ODB / ODB-II, there is a popular app called *Torque* for Android tablets. This app is configurable for the look and instrumentation you prefer, whether futuristic, steam-punk, retro, art-deco, whatever your imagination and creativity can come up with, and with whatever data is available in the data stream. There are several apps with different names and capabilities for Apple products too. You'll need an ODB adapter to use these apps.

The BMS

BMS stand for Battery Management System. It gets its own section because it works during both the charging and the discharging cycles. It can be a stand-alone system, or integrated with the SoC and Charger. Some people even consider it to be optional.

Do you need it? Technically, no. You can charge and discharge your batteries without one. Just like you can "technically" live on a diet of nothing but sugary sodas and bacon. You just won't be as healthy or live as long as you should have. The same is true for your batteries without the BMS. In fact, *not* having a good quality BMS will void the warranty on most LiFePO4 batteries.

Since batteries are mass-produced and nothing is perfect, some of your cells will charge or discharge a little faster or slower than others. Some will hold more or less of a charge too. If you want to avoid ruining your batteries prematurely, you need a good, active BMS. There are different types of BMS — *active* and *passive* are the two main categories. If you skimp and get a cheap one, it's probably passive. That's not as good. A passive BMS only monitors the high-water mark of the cells and cuts off the whole pack when any one cell reaches maximum charge or discharge, regardless of what's going on with the others. An active BMS can slow-down some cells and speed-up others to create a balance between them, bringing the whole pack to an optimal state.

Overcharging or undercharging your cells will degrade them to a fraction of their total life potential. One bad cell can also force its neighbors to overcharge or undercharge, eventually leading to a cascade of failure to the rest of the pack. If you can identify problematic cells before this happens it'll save you a lot of time, money and headache.

How it works:

Let's assume you have 48 cells in your battery. Depending on what brand of BMS you have, you'll probably have to segment this into four groups of twelve cells each. Each group will have its own monitor, and each monitor will connect to one controller.

What's missing from the photo on the facing page is the bundle of wires that connects these modules to each and every cell in your battery pack. For 12 cells, you'll have thirteen wires — one wire for each positive terminal (one on each cell), and one wire for the final negative terminal in the group.

With these wires the BMS can monitor the voltage of each independent cell, and more importantly, it can move small charges between neighboring cells to balance the whole group. If you have an integrated system, it can also communicate with the charge controller and the SoC monitor.

Programming:

Once connected, you'll need to set certain values for the BMS to monitor. These include (among other things) a high/low voltage alert, a balanced voltage range, and if your BMS has thermal monitoring capability, the acceptable temperature range for the batteries.

Programming is typically done via a USB connection to a computer, and either a software interface you can enter values into, or a command-line interface you'll have to type commands into. If you have a compatible SoC display you may be able to program key values that way without needing a computer.

If you have more cells than one BMS module can mange, you can connect multiple BMS systems together via the CAN bus. One will act as the controller, with all the others as satellites. This way you only have to program the controller.

Specific details for installing and configuring your BMS can differ among brands, so be sure to follow the instructions that come with your specific BMS system.

DC to DC converter

The last major component you need is the DC to DC converter. This confuses some people. "Why do I need to convert DC to DC?" Because voltage matters.

Your main battery pack is a high voltage system, typically somewhere between 48 volts and 192 volts. But your car's "legacy" electrical system (lights, wipers, etc.) all work at 12 volts. Normally you'll have a 12-volt battery for this. The 12-volt battery in a gas car is recharged by an alternator. In an EV, the DC-DC converter serves this purpose. When you turn on the car, the DC-DC converter steps-down the high voltage and feeds it to the 12-volt battery.

"But my friend who knows electronics said I don't really need one."

Your friend is right — if you don't care about money. Batteries are expensive to replace. The DC-DC converter will pay for itself. Here's how that works:

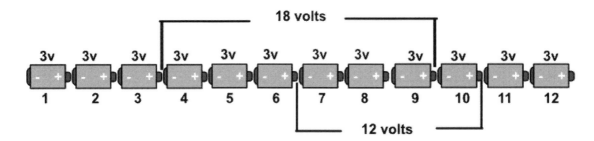

This series of cells has an end-to-end voltage of 36 volts. But you can tap anywhere you want to pull any voltage you want between 3 and 36 volts. In this case, we've tapped it for a 12-volt and an 18-volt draw.

Why this is a bad idea: Notice that cells 4, 5, 6, and 10 are all doing double-duty, and cells 7, 8, and 9 are doing triple-duty. It's like mixing different sized cells in the same pack. Some cells will top-up or hit maximum discharge before the others. You'll end up wasting some of your battery cells, and they ain't cheap. Your BMS is good, but it's probably not *that* good. Sure, you could spend extra and get a super heavy-duty extra special industrial capacity BMS, if you can find one, or just get a good DC-DC converter and a separate 12-volt battery. Do the math and it's clear that a DC-DC converter is the best solution for cost and efficiency.

The DC-DC converter I have simply connects from the HV battery on one end, and then to the 12-volt battery on the other end. There's a separate control wire that turns it on or off. The control wire goes through a relay, then to the HV positive terminal. The relay is activated by the ignition switch. (see the schematic page for details.) This will keep your 12-volt system fully charged as long as the car is on.

Section Three:

A Step-By-Step Overview

(Soon to be a major motion picture!)

Clear some space, organize your shop, get the camera ready. It's time to make things happen. I'm not going to deep-dive into specifics of how to route wires, how to attach things to your frame, where to put various components, etc. Each project will be different. In fact, if I did this exact same project again, I'd do a lot of things differently. Not because I made mistakes or wasn't satisfied, but because there are a

multitude of options, and I am curious how some of the other paths might have worked out.

I started by removing the exhaust system and the fuel tank. Get rid of the fuel first, and **DO NOT** cut into the tank when removing it. There will be explosive fumes in there. Any spark will ignite them. The path of the exhaust pipe is a great place to run conduit if you put any of your batteries or electronics in the rear.

Of course, we gotta take that old motor out. If you've never removed an engine before, there's a lot you have to disconnect: Fuel line, fuel gauge wire, water temp sensor, oil pressure sensor, battery and other electrical connections, radiator and coolant lines, throttle linkage, clutch hydraulic line, exhaust pipe, tachometer cable, speedometer cable, and probably a few other things, depending on your car. Don't be surprised if you miss one. We missed a grounding strap that almost caused some big problems while we were pulling the engine.

In our case it was necessary to remove the entire front end of the car, including the steering box. We took the opportunity to upgrade the steering to a rack-and-pinion system while we were at it. The transmission was going to stay in the car, but it was easier to remove it along with the motor and re-install it later.

This engine and transmission combo weigh over 400 lbs. An engine hoist was critical for removing it, however, the foot of the hoist was too wide to fit between the narrow wheel-base of the TR3. We had to jack the wheels off the ground so the hoist could roll underneath them.

Find a place to set your old engine out of the way. It's probably going to be there for a while. If you're planning to keep your transmission, this is a good time to disconnect the engine from the transmission.

If you have an adapter plate, check the instructions for anything special you need to do with the clutch or flywheel. We decided to eliminate the clutch and flywheel in order to simplify connecting the transmission to the motor.

Connecting the electric motor to the transmission was our first big challenge. No one makes an adapter plate for this car, so I had to make my own adapter. Here's the open end of the transmission:

The clutch alignment spindle extends 1.75 inches out from the splined portion of the shaft. I considered cutting it off, but the main shaft is worth almost as much by itself as the whole transmission. If I ever decide to eliminate the transmission and go with direct-drive, I'll want to sell it to a collector. Or, if I ever decide to revert the car back to gas for any reason, I'll be able to.

The splines on the transmission shaft are what we need to couple to, but I couldn't find a coupler that went that deep. Also, there are ten splines, which is unusual. I couldn't find any couplers to attach to ten splines. This was a real problem. After some research I discovered that the TR3 engine was originally designed to go into a tractor. After some more research I found a ten-spline tractor PTO coupler (designed for farm implements like shredders and post-hole diggers). Fortunately, it is the exact length and diameter of my shaft. The fit couldn't be more perfect. But this one didn't come with any ratings. Is it strong enough?

I used to have a tractor. I've busted a couple of PTO drive shafts, destroyed a gear box on a shredder, and had a post-hole digger almost flip my tractor over (bad operator error!) But I've never busted one of the couplers. It was a risk I was willing to take — but it was an educated risk. Now all I need is a way to attach the PTO coupler to some kind of flexible coupler.

Why flexible? — Because it's unlikely that my home-made adapter assembly will be able to align within 1/1000th of an inch or be perfectly straight. Can I find a flexible coupler that attaches to a 1.125" shaft on one end, and a 1.75" shaft on the other, that can also handle 220 Nm of torque and 7000 RPMs? I actually found *several*.

Lovejoy has a high-torque, high-RPM jaw adapter that does the job. But you can't order directly from Lovejoy, and the retailers they sent me to kept stalling or losing my order. It was frustrating. Finally I saw this little gem in the legalese section of Lovejoy's catalog:

In our conversations I had told the salespeople what I would be using it for. I guess EV car conversions fall into the "other devices" category. I wish they had told me. I wasted four weeks waiting for parts to come in that were never coming.

Fortunately I found a different product at McMaster.com that met all my requirements, and it had the added benefit of being cheaper. And I didn't need to talk to a salesperson to order it. Win-Win.

The downside to this coupler is a significantly smaller tolerance to misalignment. The next part of this challenge is getting the two pieces aligned as closely as possible.

This flexible coupler and the PTO coupler combination will add 3.25 inches of spacing I'll need between the motor face and the transmission housing. I ordered a four foot section of 3x3 square tubing and a 1/4" sheet of steel plate and some other bits of metal from MetalsDepot.com. A week later I began to fabricate my own custom adapter/spacer and a new motor mount. The encoder end of the electric motor is about nine inches away from the car's original motor mounts, so I had to add some metal plates to the car's frame for the new motor mounts. I didn't want to modify the frame itself — some governments restrict licensing for that kind of thing. The new motor mounts are bolted on with heavy-duty square-U bolts around exposed frame-beams in the engine bay. They are solid, secure, and can be removed without leaving a scratch.

IMPORTANT: *You can't just fudge this.* I have an engineering background and a lot of experience measuring and calibrating CNC machines to within 1/1000th of an inch. If you don't know how to do that, a book like this is not going to teach it to you. Find a machine shop to help you if you can, or buy an off-the-shelf adapter. If no one makes an adapter for your particular car's transmission, you can always replace the transmission with a different one. If you can't figure out how to mount your motor, **get help**. It will be a lot less expensive than a dropped driveshaft pole-vaulting your car at 60 MPH, with you in it.

  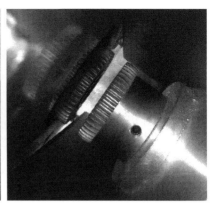

Before putting the motor and transmission back in, it was a good time to remove everything else in the car. We cleaned out the entire engine bay of everything except the brake system. Since we won't need most of the old gauges and we'll be installing new gauges that won't fit the old holes, we decided to remove the whole dashboard and craft a new one. We'll be replacing 100% of the old wiring with new wires too.

Ok, with all that out of the way, it's time to install the new motor and transmission.

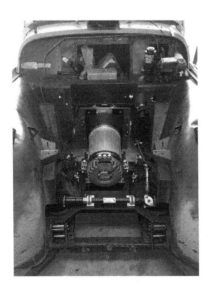 

With the new electric motor installed, we're halfway done, right? Not even close!

Take a moment to admire how much smaller the electric motor is. We're going to use the rest of that empty space for batteries and a lot of other things. First we built an aluminum platform over the motor. The platform will hold half of our batteries and the controller. The other half of the batteries will go where the gas tank used to be. Due to constraints with the steering linkage and the hood latch, we had to turn the platform at a slight angle to fit.

 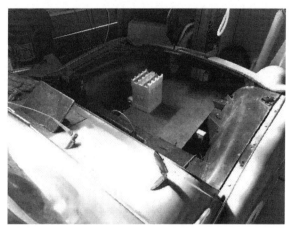

After a lot of trial and error experimenting with different arrangements and fitments, we installed all the electrical components in the engine bay and half of the battery pack. The other half will go in the back, and the master high-voltage switch is mounted under the dashboard behind the shifter stick.

It's good to do the arrangement first so you know what routes to take with your wires, and how long they'll need to be. Keep it neat. It will save you a lot of effort and frustration in the end, and will help support your resale value if you ever decide to sell the car.

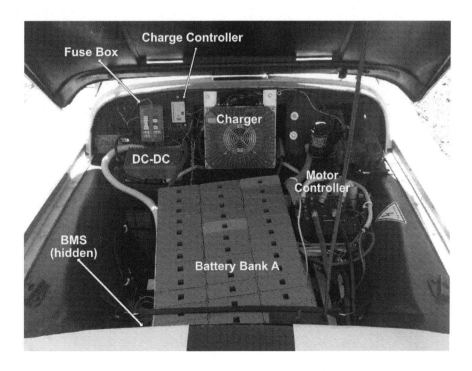

Battery bank 'B' (three rows if you look real hard) is installed where the old gas tank used to be. Previously I said that you can't just put the batteries in the trunk. You have to consider the weight distribution from front to rear. In this case, the gas tank was designed to fit in-between the trunk's forward wall and the back of the seating area. It's directly over the rear axle so I'm not adding any tail weight.

The fuel tank weighed just over 100 lbs. when full, and this battery pack weighs 177 lbs. By removing the spare tire and replacing it with a "Smart Spare" Tire Repair Kit, I saved 45 lbs. (spoke rims are heavier than steel rims.) So ultimately I'm only 32 lbs over the original weight on the rear axle. The 32 lbs. can come out of my luggage weight capacity since I don't plan on hauling any suitcases.

We removed the forward wall of the trunk (it was just a piece of carpeted plywood) and installed the battery cells there — all except for eight cells that wouldn't fit. (Since this photo was taken I found a way to make them fit, so the finished trunk will be as neat and vacant as when it was new.)

All that looks fairly neat and organized so far. But be warned… there will be wires.

You can't tell from this photo, but all the wires behind the new dash are color coded. This helps to keep them organized.

Our installation includes eight new switches, eleven indicator lights and one master switch. The master switch is under the dashboard in front of the shift lever. It disconnects the main battery pack.

In addition to the legacy functions (lights, wipers, horn…) we need switches for high and low regeneration modes (so the motor can recharge the batteries during deceleration and down hills). This function can also be activated by a proximity switch at the brake pedal if you choose. Also, forward and reverse can be switched via a toggle on the dashboard, so no transmission shifting required. Is this safe from accidental switching? Yes. If the controller senses the motor turning in one direction and you accidentally flip the switch for it to go the other way, the motor goes limp until it stops spinning. It's just as safe, maybe more safe, than a conventional car with the PRNDL shifter on the center console.

When programming the controller it is useful to disable the motor so you can test all the settings without actually spinning it. I installed a "no traction" switch for this purpose. This is different from the "zero torque" mode that temporarily disables the regeneration and acceleration when switched on. I wired the zero-torque switch to my clutch pedal using a proximity switch. It's not the same as a physical clutch, but it does make shifting on the fly easier for those rare instances I actually need it. And I installed a master switch to turn the whole 12-volt sub-system on or off, either with or without the key.

Finally, I put the charger port on the dashboard. Why? Because it wouldn't fit in the original gas fill-hole and I didn't want to cut any body panels. My project is a *fully-reversible* conversion. But consider this — it's impossible to forget to unplug it this way! Also, this is just a temporary dashboard. I plan to re-organize the layout and use a higher quality of wood later. At that time I might consider finding a new place for the charging port.

Since the TR3 has a turn signal switch and horn button on the center of the steering wheel, and I lost those when I upgrade to rack-and-pinion steering, the horn button is on the dash (lower right), and an indicator switch is installed on the dashboard behind the left side of the steering wheel (hidden behind the steering wheel). My son designed and 3D printed a new cap for the center of the steering wheel, which we painted and hand-rubbed to get a bakelite-like finish. All switches and indicator lights were found on Amazon.com or AllElectronics.com.

Programming the Controller

These screen shots are specific to the Netgain Hyper-9 HV controller. Yours may be different, but the concepts are similar. The software is capable of a lot more than what I'll show here. These are only the ones you'll want to play with first.

The controller comes with a cable that connects via USB to your Windows computer. Install and launch the software with the controller turned on. You'll see something like this.

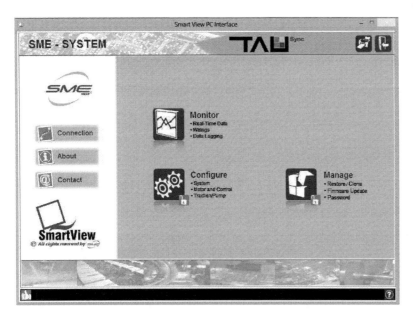

The start screen. Your configuration is stored in a file called a "clone" file. Hit the "connection" button on the left and make sure it's working. After that you'll need to click on "manage" on the right. You'll need to upload a configuration file unique to your motor to "commission" the motor. Now you can make changes.

I'll be honest. This software is flaky as hell, and you can lose a lot of work when it unexpectedly dies all of a sudden. Be sure to SAVE your changes after every change. When you're done, be sure to export your new, custom "clone" file so you can re-install it if you ever need to.

Having said that, it's a truly easy way to configure some pretty complicated things, like your throttle's acceleration profile.

Different accelerator throttles will have different outputs. You'll need to tune the acceleration profile to match your throttle's output.

Here you can set whatever curve you want. Most gas cars creep forward of you don't hold your foot on the brake. I don't like that, so I put a dead space between zero throttle and the start of acceleration.

After that, I like a steep, aggressive acceleration. You might want something more forgiving. Play with it. You can change it whenever as you like.

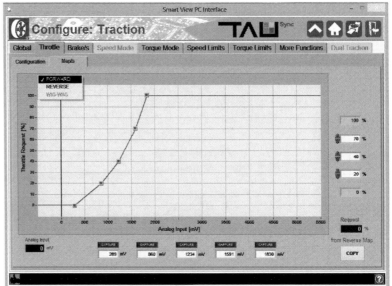

If your controller has any regeneration functions, you'll need to configure those too.

This one has three "profiles." Mine is configured for zero regen in profile one, 30% in profile two, and 60% in profile three. I can select between these via a switch on the dashboard.

60% regen is like stepping on the brake as you approach a stop sign.

30% regen feels like normal deceleration in a gas engine car.

Zero regeneration is like throwing it into neutral when you let your foot off the throttle. Your specific experiences may be different.

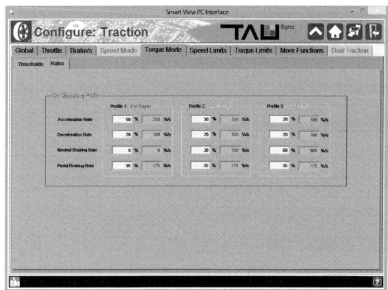

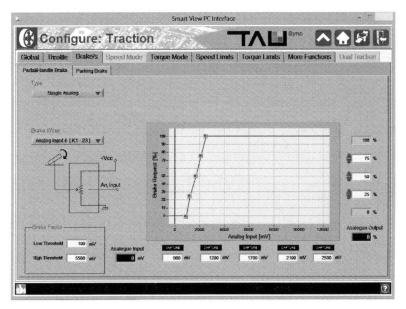

You can also configure a brake throttle to increase the percentage of regeneration depending on how far you depress the brake pedal.

The other things...

Air Conditioning & Heat

There are three main components to an air conditioner; the compressor, the condenser and the duct/fan/thermostat system. The compressor is the only part that uses power from the motor. The rest are operated from the 12-volt system. You can re-use everything except for the compressor.

12-volt electric AC compressors exist and work well, and you can put it anywhere the lines will reach. If you're converting a van or don't mind installing something on your roof, there are 12-volt fully self-contained RV air conditioners that are as easy to install as a sun roof.

Heating is where you have the most options. But be warned—generating heat takes a lot of energy. You can run down your batteries real quick with the wrong heating choice. A good hair blow-dryer takes 1650 watts of energy to run. Two of these will keep the interior of your car pretty warm, and you can feed the air right into your existing duct work. But don't do this. That's more than three kilowatts — equal to 20 amps at 144 volts. That's enough energy to propel my TR3 about 30 miles per hour.

There are multitudes of small space heaters you can choose from, but a more energy efficient solution is to NOT heat the whole car. Just heat the people instead. Heated seat covers, for instance, or a heated driving jacket. Heated jackets are common for motorcycle riders. Most are battery operated, but Harley Davidson makes one you can plug-in to your car's power-port. There are also heated pants available at sporting goods stores for hunters. For me, I got a heated seat cover off Amazon for about $25. It works great, and I can remove it for spring and summer driving.

Brake Booster

I've never had the opportunity to work with one of these, but 12-volt powered brake boosters do exist. All my projects have weighed less than 3000 lbs. and didn't need anything more than normal, ordinary hydraulic brakes. But I did upgrade the VW to front disk brakes, and that by itself made a huge difference.

Power Steering Assist

This is also something I've never worked with, but a little research will find several after-market electrically powered products via the on-line car parts retailers. They all seem to be specific to one or another make and model of car, so you'll have to see what's available for your car and how it is installed.

Having said that, I've heard that a lot of people just remove the power steering systems with Mazda Miata conversions. It's such a light-weight car is barely needs power steering at all. The steering will be a little stiffer, but a larger diameter steering wheel will give you more leverage and reduce the effort to steer — one reason why most older cars tended to have larger steering wheels. All classic cars have a functional mechanical steering linkage. Power assist is just for convenience.

Instruments

If your car, and the equipment you install, have an ODB / ODB-II interface, there is a popular app called *Torque* for Android tablets. This app is configurable for the instrumentation and appearance you prefer, whether futuristic, steam-punk, retro, art-deco, using whatever data is available in the data stream. There are several apps with different names and capabilities for Apple products too. You'll need an ODB adapter to use these apps.

Useful Links (circa 2021)

Remember, this is just a sampling to get you started. There are many, many more options than these. And as time goes on, some of these will become stale, broken or supplanted by newer, better companies. Use at your own risk!

(Also— I have not received any compensation or consideration for any of these links. This is simply a list I compiled during my own conversion project. Nothing more.)

EV specific product and service companies:

ElectricCarPartsCompany.com
*(Carl generously spent an hour on the phone with me one day.
A very helpful, very knowledgable man. Highly recommended.)*

Thunderstruck-EV.com
(These guys were also extremely helpful.)

MomentMotors.com
(Marc Davis was by far the most helpful person in this whole process.)

EVWest.com

CanEV.com (adapter kits)

Go-EV.com (Netgain Motors)

HPEVS.com (HPEVS motors)

CurtisInstruments.com

Power transmission:

www.DirectIndustry.com

www.lovejoy-inc.com

www.NorthwestFab.com

Misc.

AllElectronics.com

EVSEadapters.com

McMaster.com

Granger.com

MetalsDepot.com

Car specific parts:

MossMotors.com (Triumph, MG, Mini, Austin Healey, Jaguar)

MossMiata.com (Miata)

Jbugs.com (Volkswagen)

MTMFG.com (Volkswagen)

Carparts.com

Jegs.com

SummitRacing.com

Master Wiring Diagram
(EV Components only)

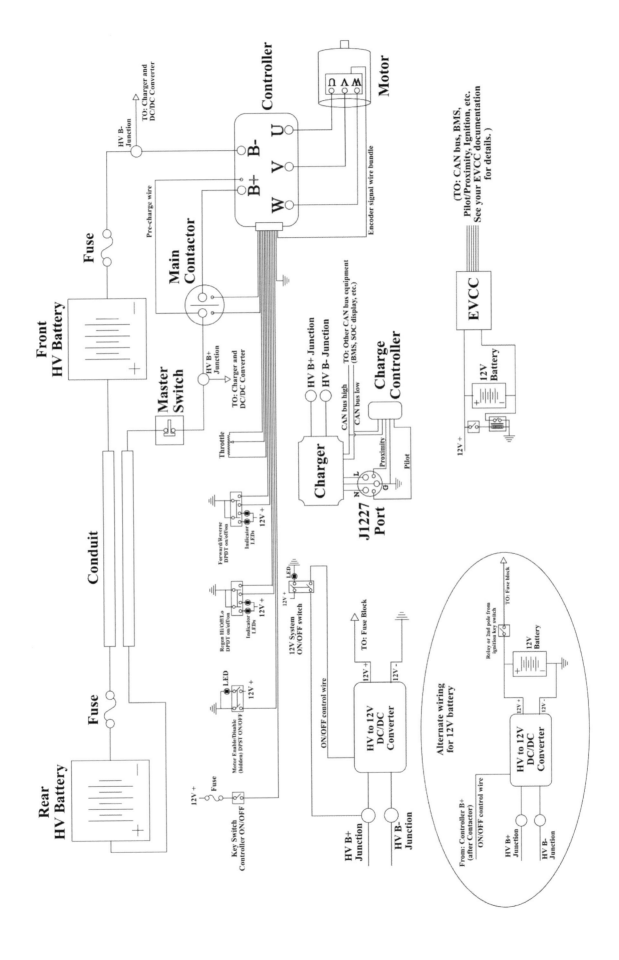

Made in the USA
Columbia, SC
30 July 2021